Sweeping It Under The Drug

A Complete Book About `Recreational` Drugs
And
How To Create A Satisfying Life Without Them

By

Dennis Marcellino

Lighthouse Publishing
P.O. Box 220
Reseda, California 91335

Sweeping It Under The Drug

A Complete Book About 'Recreational' Drugs
And
How To Create A Satisfying Life Without Them

Published By

Lighthouse Publishing
P.O. Box 220
Reseda, California 91335

Library of Congress Cataloging in Publication Data
    Marcellino, Dennis, 1948-
      Sweeping It Under The Drug: a complete book about
      'recreational drugs' and how to create a satisfying
      life without them/ by Dennis Marcellino
          p.   cm.
      Bibliography: p.
      Includes index.
      ISBN 0-945272-04-9 (softcover)
      ISBN 0-945272-05-7 (hardcover)
      1. Substance abuse--prevention
      2. Dependency (psychology)
      3. Self-actualization (psychology)
      I. Title
      HV4998.M37 1988
      362.2'9--dc 19   88-2083 CIP

This book is dedicated
To all of the sincere, hungry hearts
who love and earnestly seek

"The Truth"

Acknowledgments

The readers of this book are benefitting from many unseen comments from my family and friends, who made me aware of some word and structure problems, and of some viewpoints that I overlooked and needed to include if I was going to give my coverage of this topic a full and complete treatment. Their viewpoints ranged the gamut of approach-to-drugs, and all had something unique to offer. Their frank, insightful and supportive comments also let me see the importance and impact of this work, and gave it some momentum in the initial stages when I wondered what kind of affect it would have.

Therefore I'd like to thank: Nancy Marcellino, Mark and Janice Stefani, Mitch Margo, Jeff and Kathy Letchworth, Louie Nicolaides, Dan Poynter (for his business short-cuts and advice), Henry Trist (for his technical help and support), and last, but not least, my wife and in-house (literally) editorial staff, Pat Marcellino.

About The Author

In the middle 1960's, Dennis Marcellino was an award- winning math and engineering student in San Francisco. Then the hippie movement came along and he was enticed by it and joined the band wagon; literally. He left his engineering career and became a musician. He eventually worked his way up and became a member of some of the top bands of the day (The Electric Flag, The Elvin Bishop Group, Sly & The Family Stone, and Rubicon), and became a part of the drug scene that was the norm for the times.

But his analytical abilities from his math and engineering days didn't abandon him, and they let him see what was and wasn't working about the lifestyles of the times that he was in. And being a seeker of the highest pleasures that this life has to offer, he found himself thoroughly engulfed in a search to find where they existed, being driven and guided in and out of many different social groups (and their drug and highness-seeking approaches), driven by his heart's desire for high feelings, and guided by his heart's sense of truth and his mind's ability to spot contradictions.

Now he says that he's discovered enough of life's truths to where drugs are no longer needed or desired. In this book he wants to show how a person can be free of drugs and have a very satisfied heart and life. And he gives all of the minute details, covering every aspect of life, that are needed to create these.

Besides being an author, he is also currently a member of "The Tokens" ("The Lion Sleeps Tonight"). He is 40 years old, living with his wife of 23 years, and has 3 sons.

He has attended and received degrees in psychology and engineering from: San Francisco City College, Santa Monica College, Marin Holistic Psycotherapy Institute, Los Angeles Valley College, Pierce College and California State University at Northridge.

TABLE OF CONTENTS

THE INSPIRATION

THE SOLUTION

Preface

This book has been set up like spring cleaning (of a person's mind, heart and life). That is, first we take a look at how dirty their house might be, and we analyze it's mess. Next it is shown what a clean house would look like and how nice it would feel. And finally, a game plan is laid out by which the house can be made clean.

In terms of the subject matter of this book (eliminating drugs, and personal growth), this is how this book is laid out. First, in chapter 1, the concept: 'sweeping it under the drug' is defined. In Chapter 2, the current state of the war on drugs is discussed.

The next section is called <u>The Problem</u>. Chapters 3 through 10 discuss *why* people take drugs, what the *real* problems are, the physical realities of drugs, and some horror stories of drug use gone bad.

The next section is called <u>The Inspiration</u>. Chapters 11 through 16 describe how life was designed to be lived, i.e. how our relationships and actions would be manifesting if we were perfectly in tune with *nature's optimum design*. To the degree that we are in tune is the degree that we experience it's positive rewards (e.g. peace, satisfaction, happiness, etc.). To the degree that we aren't in tune is the degree that we experience it's negative feedback (e.g. dissatisfaction, confusion, compulsion, tension, stress, unhappiness, etc., all of which can be breeding grounds for drug use).

Finally, chapters 17 through 22 are <u>The Solution</u>. Herein lies the specific instructions on how to make the transition from 'the problem' to the 'inspiration'. I saved it for the end of the book because I first wanted to establish an identity and burden for the problem, then a hope for a solution, and then the release and satisfaction of the solution.

The best way to read the book is from start to finish without jumping ahead (which would be like seeing the end of a movie in the beginning. For it to have it's proper impact and effectiveness it has to be set up).

Good luck in carrying out (and helping others carry out) the solutions. And thank God there is a way (for a while I was starting to think that there wasn't).

Chapter 1
Sweeping It Under The Drug:
Defining The Concept

A key to us experiencing peace, happiness and satisfaction in this life is in our ability to *only* follow our natural inclinations, and not follow the unnatural ones. But how many of us are really able to do that? And, for that matter, how many even know how to tell the difference between natural and unnatural? How many add *things* on, possibly to be more personable in this hyper, modern world that we live in? Or how many suppress *things*, in order to avoid criticism, rejection, 'keep peace' or manipulate a situation? (By *things* I mean: emotions, personality traits, inclinations, thoughts, words and actions.) Or how many have bought the heavily advertised lures to fun in this world hook, line and sinker and then try to use force to get the mind, body, emotions and conscience to cooperate in allowing us to live them out? Well we probably do all of these to some degree, and a lot without even realizing it. But being unnatural like this is not easy, because the body, mind, conscience and emotions will resist. But instead of facing and dealing with their feedback, we often try to **sweep it under the drug.** (From now on when I use the term *drug* I may not only be speaking of chemical drugs but also anything that serves this function). We try to anesthetise it out of existence so that we can cruise on automatic pilot and do what we (think we) want. But this approach ultimately doesn't work and usually causes great harm to ourselves and others, while on it's way to burying us in deeper pits. Besides, the accumulation that we build under our 'rug' will constantly push to free itself, which will cause us to further turn to stronger drugs and/or more intense doses. Only when we learn to naturally respond to our inner workings can we be free of having any inclination towards drugs.

In this book I want to:
1) Show how the **sweep it under the drug** process manifests.
2) Show how we rob ourselves and others of true peace and happiness by doing it.
3) Show what *natural* is.
4) Show how to get through the withdrawals of the various drugs.
5) Show how to make the transition to a natural life (regardless of one's circumstances).

I'm also here waving a red warning sign saying that what might be fun and an escape at first could take you into some of the most painful and damaging experiences that you can't even imagine. And these experiences would take you completely by surprise (graphic stories are included as examples).

So let's take an inner journey together and see how much more of ourselves we can clean up and how much more natural, happy, fulfilled and at peace we can be. And out of the strength and positive experience that will result from manifesting the proper actions, thoughts and words, not only will we be able to say no to drugs, but their 'highs' will look like lows to us.

Chapter 2
The Current State Of The
'War On Drugs'

I watch the "say no to drugs" commercials on T.V. and I respect and admire the concern and effort. I wonder, though, how effective they are in combatting the current drug problem? Hopefully they are being a countervoice (but still I wonder how strong) to the seducing voices in people's lives who say that drugs are fun, and that drugs are an answer. The answer to my wondering comes when I watch the local news and see how the police show up at a local high school with a puppet show and an anti-drug speaker, but only 20 students sprinkle the auditorium and are divided by many empty seats. And these students all look like the so-called 'good kids' who would never take drugs anyway. Once again, I respect and admire the effort, but I don't think you can charm away very deep seated and complex problems. Besides, in terms of peer pressure, the opposition is vicious.

Also, the "Just Say No" foundation's sphere of influence is just young people (ages 7 to 14). And their role, it seems, is to create an alternative peer group to the drug-using group so that school-age children will have a supportive place to hang out when they do say no. This is extremely needed and I applaud them and wish them much success. But what about the kids who already are into drugs? And, for that matter, what about teens and adults?

Being an ex-drug user myself, realistically, I know that most drug users don't have the strength to be able to say no to drugs. This phrase can only be effective for those who do have the strength and are just toying with the idea of taking drugs. It's to help warn them of the potential dangers that drugs themselves can create, and that you can end up at a point where you won't have your strength to rely on anymore. This phrase can only help to slow down the growth of a spreading cancer. But what about the giant problem of the already existing cancer? Like Bruce Springsteen said: "Everybody has a hungry heart". And I'm saying that only a naturally full, satisfied heart with a good, ongoing support system can say no to drugs. A support system that doesn't have 'unnatural behavior' as a prerequisite for membership in it.

So the real problem then is the 'states of the hearts' of the people who use (and are candidates to use) drugs. And the real solution is knowing how to attain (and maintain) a full, satisfied heart naturally, without having to resort to the temporary highs and peace of drugs (which are usually followed by equivalent or greater lows).

In the current attack on the drug problem that's going on in this country, I see something that is very necessary for the solution of the problem missing. That's one of the main reasons I wrote this book. I see a lot of police raids, warning ads, etc., but I don't see anybody addressing the real causes of the problem (heart, job, social, family, cultural, relationship, moral and environmental problems). And therefore, I don't see real solutions that are going to be effective being offered. Being a cleaned up (from drugs) person, I can sympathize with the efforts of the N.B.A., 'Dare to say no' television commercials, etc., and I can understand the way they are seeing things. But from an ex-drug user's perspective, I don't see anyone talking to the drug user's heart in terms of what they're experiencing and dealing with, or giving them the visions that will give them the power to stop using drugs. "Say no to drugs" is a much too *simple* approach to a very *complex* problem. The T.V. ads that I see are a very *shallow* approach to a very *deep* problem. The actors, sports stars and celebrities (although they might mean well) come off as phoney and insincere (the hippie term was *plastic*), which is the exact thing that many drug users have been burned by and are trying to escape. (A more precise description of *plastic* would be: the hyper, insensitive, greedy, loveless, putting-on-an-act, dog-eat-dog air of

12

competition and stressful survival). I kind of think that drug users are laughing and scorning these commercials in which people dance and sing " say no to drugs ". They are probably laughingly saying to themselves "you want me to give up drugs for that?" (with "that" being hyper, unnatural, trying-to-be-in-with-the-modern-genre joy). Hopefully this book will start filling this 'understanding/-solutions' void in the world.

In this book I will spell out the problems and their causes; and I will also spell out solutions. It is my desire to try to save people from the pains and pitfalls that I went through because of drugs (and also because of not knowing how to correctly live this life), and to show them how to have a naturally peaceful and satisfied heart.

Some people opt for certain drugs based on hope, while others do so because of peer pressure. But some make a choice to continue with drugs based on a few initial highs and relieving experiences. But I equate this with walking into an African jungle because of a few tasty berries at the outskirts. I'm trying to warn of the giant, ferocious beasts in the jungle, whose attacks may come as a shock, and whose attacks may not be survived (as many haven't). I'm lucky, I did. But I experienced so much extreme suffering and damage that I want to warn of these also. To the drug users I'd like to say: have hope. Because there is a solution to all of your problems and needs. And even have a greater hope. Because there is a greater peace and satisfaction awaiting you than you ever thought was naturally possible. And it's something that you're naturally hungry for and driven towards. It's the reason you take drugs. And it's available to every single one of us; no exceptions. I'm here to say that I found it (in spite of the fact that , for a long time, I was very cynical, skeptical and hopeless) and so can you. But you'll need a solid vision and game plan to achieve it. But that's what this book is all about; to give you that.

Parents....And If Their Kids Are Taking Drugs
Some drug specials on television are advising parents to get tough with their kids and "save" them from drugs. They say that kids are "still in the woods", as far as how-to-live-life goes, until they become adults. But what if the

parents are also still in the woods (and most of them are)? Them getting tough with their children is only imprisoning them until they can escape (which might be sooner than the parents think), and broadening the gap between the parents and their children.

The solution here is the same as that with a teething infant who is putting paper in his mouth, which he could possibly choke on. You first interest them in a teething ring, which isn't dangerous yet it still satisfies their need. And then while their attention is moving towards the teething ring, it will be moving away from the paper.

Problems happen when parents don't have a teething ring to offer. Their only options then become to (1)hide their eyes and let the baby play with the paper, with the potential of them eating it and choking on it; or (2)get tough, take away the paper, and leave the infant crying, wallowing in their need. But really though, neither of these are adequate or optimum solutions.

Well I'm happy to say that this book will give the 'teething ring' to both the parents and the children (and all drug users for that matter).

The Gap Is Bridged In The War On Drugs

On one side you have the drug users and dealers, who have been (and are) one of the main causes of so many of this nation's (and the world's) problems, e.g. crime, AIDS, auto accidents, disease, death, illegitimate pregnancies, mental and emotional illnesses, financial losses, etc..

On the other side you have those who are concerned about the drug problem and run ads that tell a person to "say no to drugs", "D.A.R.E. to say no", etc..

But the overall problem just keeps getting worse. There's a giant **gap** between these two sides. Why? It's because these public efforts to eliminate drug use are just 'issuing commands', and not really offering solutions to the 'heart' and 'mind' problems that drive people to use drugs. They are not offering the needed alternatives (that will really work) and showing how to transform one's life to them. And like I've said, most drug users don't have the strength to be able to "say no to drugs". They would need something more satisfying to say **yes** to simul-

14

taneously (the 'teething ring' analogy). Something that would handle their problems, and fill the void that makes them seek satisfaction in drugs. Drug use isn't the real problem. Knowing how to live this life is.

With this book, I've bridged this gap. The solutions to the heart and mind problems of drug users are shown, and all the way to the deepest levels. 'You haven't really gotten rid of a weed unless you've pulled it out roots and all'. The ways to enact these solutions are also shown.

I was a young adult searching for the true answers as to what this life is all about and how it should be lived. But I had to painfully go through this world's mazes of untruth before I finally found those answers. Now, by writing this book, I want to save anyone that I can from going through troubles like the ones that I went through, because it's not necessary to have to go through them if you know how to live this life correctly. Similarly, if you know how to operate and take care of a car, you can eliminate many troubles that you would have otherwise had. Well the design of this life and our bodies (including emotions, mind, etc.) are just as precise and definable as any specific car. And this design is not open for debate or modification. In this book I'll describe the specifics of this design.

Chapter 3
An Overview Of The Problem

Webster's Dictionary:
drug-1) any substance used as a medicine.
medicine-3a) any substance used in treating, healing
    or relieving pain.

All of us are going through life with *continuous* problems (major and/or subtle) as well as the *day to day* problems. A certain percentage of these we face, deal with and resolve. The remaining percentage we put on hold, put on a back burner or just plain try to avoid. But these problems just won't go away and, with a force proportional to their urgency, they'll start pushing on our mind, conscience, and emotions (which, if avoided too long, can create physical problems). So now, in this back-burner-approach to our problems, we are faced with either having to now face, deal with and resolve the problem(s), or take stronger action to suppress them. The natural time allotted for putting them off has run out and now we must satisfy them, or use a 'foreign device' and enter into the *unnatural* realm. Any of these foreign devices will henceforth be called a drug. But in addition to serving this function, some drugs occasionally create positive feelings and insights. But the premise of this book is that all of this can be had naturally without having to suffer any of the negative effects of drugs.

These self, peer or socially prescribed medicines for our dis-eases are merely temporary solutions that end up causing greater problems. They merely put the problems out of sight temporarily while the user then hopes to experience the good feelings that are really meant to be the natural rewards for living a right life.

Problems may be swept under the drug, but this rug is a thin one. And when the problems resurface again, they bring a whole corp of ugly cohorts with them, such as: withdrawal, hangovers, physical dependency, paranoia, emotional problems, out of touch with reality, poverty, crimes to pay for, broken homes, lost relationships, guilt and low self esteem from the mistreatment of others and self, physical deterioration, health problems, mental health problems, etc., etc..

In many cases a person is swept away by the crowd and just *finds* his or her self taking a drug approach to life. The major problems happen when they find that they've been swept away by the drug. Or when they find that they've trained their 'initial response to their problems' to be: 'sweep them under a drug' (i.e. push them out of consciousness, and keep them there with a drug), rather than 'turn to the problems and solve them'.

Earlier I said that we were going through life with *continuous* problems. These can be further subdivided into two groups: (1) those that have their origins in recent memory; and (2) those whose origins we can't remember. The problems in the second group have been buried so long that we aren't even aware of having them. Yet the constant subconscious suppression that is required to hold them in check alters our personality, robs us of energy and denies us many of life's positive feelings.

This second group can be very tough to deal with. And because a person is dealing with the invisible and the unknown, they are more likely to opt for drugs out of sheer frustration from dealing with emotional pressure from a source that is indistinguishable. But the quickest way to solve these problems is not the psychoanalytical approach of dwelling on the past and digging for the roots of the problems. Too much trauma is re-experienced in this process and a deeper pit may be created. Why not just do what inevitably has to be done anyway? And that is, change our behavior to the proper actions required by nature for the given areas in our lives that we are having problems in. I think that the reason that this happens so infrequently is because most people don't know what these proper actions are. I certainly don't see this wisdom or understanding being reflected in the media or most of the psychological professions to any more than a very small degree.

One of the reasons I'm writing this book is because I've traveled some of the drug routes and they *don't work*. And I'd like to spare anyone that I can the miseries and horrors of going these routes, and help bring back those who already have. (Of course all of this couldn't be done unless I also showed the natural routes that *do work*. This is what I mainly see missing from other attempts at drug { and life } rehabilitation. This lack of knowledge about nature is the greatest ill of our world). Drugs give the hope and illusion of a quick fix to life's problems at first, but only end up creating even greater problems.

HAPPINESS

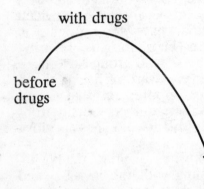

with drugs

before
drugs

Individual's curves may vary in spots but this is the general curve.

At this point you still have the original problems plus all the problems of the drugs and the aftermath of the damage they've caused.

DESPAIR

Of course I wouldn't just write this book to point out and put down the evils of drug use. An early realization that drugs ultimately didn't work, combined with a high desire for the good feelings that life had to offer, and a strong distaste for falseness and negativity, fueled a search that has resulted in a lot of understanding of the mechanics involved in transforming our lives in a positive direction. This is what I want to pass on here. Because, in the final analysis, only a satisfied heart, an ability to deal with life's problems, and an ability to create happiness in one's life can give a person the strength to say no to drugs. When you're sitting in a positive position *any* drug only brings you down. And no one would *consciously* opt to be brought down (I say consciously because you could consciously choose to engage in a drug, hoping for a high, but because of drug-takings large Russian roulette factor, you could be brought down).

I haven't taken any *major* drug (marijuana, alcohol, cocaine, heroin, LSD, downers, nicotine, caffeine, etc.) for 12 years now (with the exception of about 6 times sprinkled over the years just to make sure I wasn't missing out on anything, and to remind myself of what the experiences were and what they meant). Back then, I decided to listen to the feedback that my body was giving me and realized that drugs really weren't affecting my overall life in a good way, but rather just something that I haphazardly found myself doing. I was a musician in San Francisco in the late 1960's and the '70's and it would have been virtually impossible to avoid taking drugs. Even so, I was never a serious drug user, just a drug experimenter and social drug taker. But I did have enough experience with drug use to realize the process and the consequences. And that is, (the process:) drugs can create better states in us by making us numb to the negative feedback that we're getting from our natural drives, pace and inclinations that we're not handling correctly. But, (the consequences:) the longer that we try to see and use drugs as a solution to these drives, pace and inclination problems, we allow a gnawing negative feeling to fester underneath (feedback-backup-accumulation-on-hold) { not to mention the deterioration of health, finances and potential dangers, that I'll mention throughout the book }. But all that this gnawing negative feeling wants us to do is to enact real solutions to our real problems (and when you start taking a look, you might discover that there is quite a backlog, going all the way back to infancy). I would equate taking a drug approach with: being too lazy to throw out little bits of garbage and just throwing them under the rug on the floor. This gets the garbage out of sight temporarily, but after a while, the odor builds up to a point where it's unbearable and must be dealt with. This is why drugs aren't a real solution. They just put off the inevitable, or death happens, whichever comes first. And who knows what the consequences of a drug-users death would be, given that a drug approach to life is a rejection of nature and the mental and emotional feedback that it tries to give to get a person to live in accordance with it's plan. But after death, nature must be faced and the consequences must be paid. I mean, nature allows us to overrule it in a minor way with drugs and harmful treatment of ourselves and others, but does anyone think that they have the power to out-heavy the power that created this *immense* and extremely intricate universe? Or to avoid whatever it has planned for them? And even if you think that " when it ends it ends ", know that you are making a very risky decision with that philosophy.

Another analogy of the drug-approach would be: A person who's afraid of the dentist and dislikes the experience so much that, when they get a toothache, they rub on Orajel or Campho-Phenique to numb away the ache. Eventually, because the decay was allowed to set in to a much greater degree while working under an unseen blanket, the person has to either go through a much more painful dental procedure such as a root canal, or face the heavy pain and discomfort of extractions and dentures when, initially, a simple filling would have done the job.

So, given all of this, I forced and allowed myself to live with the gnawing negativity that I had been using drugs to run from. I did this because I hoped that it's pain and discomfort would drive me to find the solutions as to how to end these feelings. They did, and after a 15 year search, I've found these solutions. Now I've been living without any gnawing negative feeling building up for 6 years. I experience peace of mind, heart and conscience to a greater degree than I ever have. And now I want to pass on how I acquired them, maintain them and make them grow. Because the rules and principles are the same for the basic design of the human mind, body and heart and can be applied to all. What I'm talking about here is the process of how to clean up the present, keep the present clean, and work on cleaning up past problems that have been submerged (and are influencing the present in a negative way).

In this sense, this book can be valuable to everyone because, once you're experiencing the rewards of being rid of the major drugs, you become inspired to clean up further and seek more rewards. You want the best that life has to offer. And what getting into this fine art essentially means is: a lifelong process of discovering and eliminating the *minor* drugs (T.V., sports {as a spectator}, food, aberrant personality traits { such as gossip, worry and hyperness }, etc.. < See chapter 8 >). As I will clarify later, there is a perfect working order to this life and everything and everyone in it. And there is a continual, perfect flow (of energy and direction) going on in everyone every second, which confirms our participation in this order (one of the feelings that validate whether we're in this flow or not is 'inspiration'). To the degree that we're in and stay in this flow is the degree that we are drug free. Besides being a chemical that can alter our experience, a 'drug' can be anything that we might turn to in lieu of turning to this flow. It can be a behavior pattern, a habit, an unnatural personality trait, an outer focus, an activity, etc.. In many instances, this flowing river of perfection may get pushed to deep subterranean levels, as we frantically, hyperly and/or compulsively <u>push</u> ourselves through unconnected activities. In this sense, <u>we are all drug addicts</u>, to some degree. We may be starting from different points of ability - to - be - in - this - flow and inner - cleanness (even without having *any* major drugs in our life), but we <u>all</u> have something to work on.

The other half of this fine art is: to fill the voids left by the elimination of the minor drugs with discovering and taking on, more and more, the *natural* ways of being (acting out these ways gets us back into the flow). And then just enjoying the ever increasing rewards for just being natural: peace, cleanness, purpose, love, happiness, etc..

Chapter 4
A Problem Of The Heart

Many say we have a drug problem in the world today. But I think that this is like saying we have an abortion problem. Both are mis-labellings and shallow views of the real problems. Drugs and abortion are the weeds of deeper roots. And why try to continually mow weeds that are growing faster and faster. They need to be pulled out by the roots. This book deals with the roots. The root of the abortion problem is a morals problem (If anyone thinks the sexual revolution was progress, just look at the regressive fruit that it's produced: abortion, A.I.D.S., V.D., the deterioration of the family, etc.). At the roots of the drug problems are *heart* problems. Many strong, satisfied hearts never opt for drugs. Drugs are medicine for the heart. They alter moods and change feelings. That is their specific function. But a satisfied heart doesn't need or want to be altered. Let's take a look at some of the outer and inner turmoil that people want to have changed.

Coming out of childhood is a prime time of being susceptible to drugs. The reason being that many are so supercharged with emotion that they can't see straight. The ones who are so charged are the ones who are prime targets for drugs. Other prime targets are those who can't see their way to normalcy and/or can't see how to make it happen. Another category are those who have been dominated and forced far away from their natural selves. They've lost their sensitivity and ability to go inside for direction, and they usually look for a replacement dictator as a source of guidance (how to break this will be shown later in the book). They attach to a person or group and go along with whatever opinions and behavior that the person or group requires. Unfortunately, many groups these days require some sort of drug involvement. All three of these are heart problems that can be solved in other ways without having to resort to drugs. But finding these ways, and how to physically pull them off, can be quite difficult. Hopefully this book will be an inspiration and a guide to make this task easier. The first step is to look at and understand your heart.

Teen Rebellion
    Why is there such an influential rebellious element in each new generation of teens? Even when all it does sometimes is imitate the rebellious teens of two generations prior (e.g. new wave/beatniks, '80's/'50's, etc.). The reason is they are leaving childhood with some scars and negative feelings, and they are entering adulthood with a fresher perspective. They haven't totally bought into the compromises with nature that the last generation did, and they don't want to. Their heart shows them what the current adults are doing wrong and they just aren't going to submit to this repulsive, unnatural behavior. But, unfortunately, most end up succumbing. But not without a fight, and not without leaving their impact by altering what's acceptable and what's not. The problem here though is that when you rebel against something, you have to replace it with something else. This something else usually isn't as obvious as the ugliness being rebelled against, and usually a more harmful situation is created than the one being rebelled against. Thus emotional turmoil and a breeding ground for drugs.
    Another problem is that teen rebellion is sometimes a blanket rebellion against everything, coupled with a confusion of not knowing how to live, and fueled by a hopelessness of what to try because of not having seen marriages and lives that really work (more breeding ground). And what fans the flames are the powerful emotions of sex, anger and pain (from having been abused by 'the giants' and aberrant peers { who are imprints of aberrant giants }). Add to this the fact that the entertainment industry knows that they can make a quick buck by providing sublimated, spinning wheels, saccharin releases for these powerful feelings, and you've got a real mess.
    Later in the book I'm going to show how to deal with these feelings. I'm also going to give some solid direction

as to how we should work, and what actions will bring peace and happiness. Hopefully this will give hope and inspire some independent crusades to achieve them. Nobody has to compromise. Anyone can be free to follow every bit of realness deep in their heart. You need to stop making the aberrant world *right* and your natural feelings *wrong*. It should be the other way around. But first you've got to know how to make this happen, and then how to carry it out.

On a recent T.V. talk show , here is what some teens had to say.

When asked if Len Bias' death, 'Say No To Drugs' campaign, etc. had any effect on drug users one teen answered: "These aren't effective. Because many teens on drugs <u>don't care</u>". That includes if they die or not. They still have their problems, and they see drugs as a solution. But in many cases, now *drugs* have become their main problem (i.e. how to get them, and avoiding withdrawal).

When asked "Didn't a teacher or other students smell the alcohol on your breath?", the student answered "70% of the students in my high school are high." (I guess that's why they call it *high* school.< Just joking >).

One said: "Peer group is real important. You want to look cool. Make a name for yotpself. But once into drugs, the drugs take over."

Another revealed a surprisingly common source of drugs and alcohol. " A lot of times we'll get our drug's from someone's parent who is also into drugs. Either they'll turn us on or we'll steal them from them." This is one of the more unfortunate snowball effects passed on from generation to generation.

The psychologist on this talk show said: "There are alarming statistics as to how practically all drug addicts, prostitutes, and homosexuals have a history of physical and sexual abuse. They already feel so down, these normally heavy moves are just small steps for them".

Lack Of Love At Home

A major culprit in all of this is a lack of real love at home. And what is 'real love'? It's just the joy, pleasure, sharing, sensitivity, burden, caring, commitment and support of letting a person be what they are naturally meant to be. The sun is just there and sits in the sky, and the flower just grows. It's that simple. And this love has a magical power to give a person the strength to say no to what's not good for them. But the inability of parents, friends, bosses, mates, strangers and ourselves to fulfill this is one of the main causes of the problems in the world today. And with each perversion or lack of love comes an equal and opposite reaction in the personality and emotional development of those who just happen to be around. And this is especially so in childhood, where the automatic-pilot computer is mostly programmed as to what our emotional reactions, communication patterns, buttons, self-image, etc. are going to be. And these aberrant traits that are taken on under much duress, and subsequently acted out many times, become very grooved into the brain and are very tough to get rid of. But it can be done. Just like editing a computer program (which, in essence, is what they are), you must first find the problem (debugging), call it up, find the solution, and then erase or replace it in the program with the proper action (not as easy as it sounds, but very inspiring to do).

Let's look at why we would even allow these bad programs to get into our brain in the first place.

First, there's an 'imprinting' factor very early in childhood where a child is only capable of instinct and imitating those around them. They don't have the ability to logically discern right from wrong. They just find themselves swimming in the 'family vibe' pool, and are tinted by the color of the water.

Next, looking at it from a young person's perspective, they need the aforementioned love to grow. But if they aren't getting it, they'll subvert their own self love to do the actions required by the parents (and older siblings and peers) in order to get their love. In dealing with a more intense situation, their rock bottom survival instinct says that they need the 'giants' to pay rent, get food, drive the car, deal with the other giants, etc.. And sometimes they have to 'add on' (to their behavior) and 'suppress' in order to keep from being hit and treated meanly in emotional and verbal ways. Usually a parent will be consistent in their unnatural expectations (because those expectations are based on what they 'believe' a child should be like, and/or their own imprinting), and therefore this consistent pressure to act unnaturally, although under protest at first, becomes grooved into the brain, buried in the subconscious automatic-pilot, forgotten and beyond easy control anymore. A lot of times, people who hate themselves and have low self esteem, are really hating these traits. Once these traits are eliminated and replaced with good ones, self hatred leaves and self like returns.

Chapter 5
Why People Take Drugs

Most of our life is being run by the 'automatic-pilot' function of our brain. That is, our responses are instantaneous and mostly unconscious when originated. It would have to be this way. Many immediate responses are needed in life, and we just don't have the conscious capacity or the time to have lengthy internal moral and policy debates about what our every thought, word, action or feeling is going to be (let alone run our breathing, circulation, facial expression, ambulation, etc.). Yet at points along the way in our lives, these moral and policy debates happened (that is, if we were given the freedom to have them. More than likely our morals and policies were forced on us). This natural brain programming ability is necessary because of our limited conscious capacity vs. the constant responses demanded in our lives. But a lot of the programming that was forced on us is not going to be in tune with our natural inclinations. Thus, inner conflict, which causes tension. Because: which of the conflicting policies is going to win?

Let's look at how our brain functions like a computer. With a computer, you:

1) ask it a question. Then;
2) much unseen tabulation and data checking goes on, and;
3) an answer is kicked out which
4) can be read on the monitor.

Similarly, with the brain:

1) a stimulus (inner or outer) is presented to the person,
2) much unseen checking of attitudes, experiences, morals, policies, etc. goes on,
3) a response is enacted within the person which
4) can be read in their actions.

It should be noted that the time elapsed between 1) and 4) in both cases is no more than a few seconds. At this point I'd like to *highly* recommend a discipline that I have been practicing (and working to get better at) for 20 years. It is absolutely prerequisite in a person who is serious about growing. And that is: *inserting and developing a step 2a)*. In computer programming talk, this would be inserting a debugging program (or qualifying step) between lines 2) and 3). In plain language this means:

    A) check your 'gut level' and your conscience to see if the response about to be given feels right.

    B) If it doesn't, try to stop the action.

    C) Put it on your list of priorities to find out what was wrong; and what would be right. Then the next time B) comes up: program the wrong out and program the right in.

Now back to our analysis. The brain response in 3) has two characteristics to it: *feeling*, and *verbal* (which is an explanation of the *feeling*). The *feelings* should be good ones, and the *verbal* should be harmonious with self and life. Unfortunately though, a lot of it isn't this way.

From raising children of my own, I can see that most feelings and attitudes in life are formed in early childhood. (The only things that can alter these in the future are survival shocks, drastic environmental changes and conscience. But even how we respond to these is greatly determined in childhood).

The way an infant's needs are dealt with is critical to the overall attitude that they will approach life with. If a baby's cries are respected and answered, and their needs are met, they'll approach life with a secure, calm, happy, loving feeling. (A quick note here about a baby's crying and the philosophy that says to let them cry. Either this philosophy is wrong, or nature is wrong to have built this alarm into them and then have it go off when it does. Infants aren't contrived enough yet to just do something for no reason. My experience says that there is always a reason why an infant cries. Either it's wet, hungry, needs to be burped or just wants to be held. And when these things are done it stops crying immediately { with the exception of colic and teething. But you still don't leave them alone to cry with these. They need you to comfort them (which you're going to have a hard time doing unless you yourself are comfortable and in love)}. The problem with the parents who hold the 'let them cry' philosophy is that they're too mentally dominated and not sensitive enough to nature { both of these problems, and their solutions, will be dealt with in this book }, or they're too selfish or enturbulated to be able to love and devote themselves to their newborn { and newborn's do require a total commitment of time and energy. But, of course, they do compensate for this with cuteness and love }. If a baby's needs are unanswered soon and they're allowed to cry too long, they'll experience distrust, anger, pain, feeling unloved, desperation and insecurity. And then as they grow older, if they're forced to suppress these feelings in order to keep peace with the 'giants', they become hyper, because they're sitting on a powder keg of repressed emotions. And the more the repression, the greater the gush of hyper energy. If on top of all of this they draw mean responses from their parents, they'll develop secrecy, experience emotional pain, depression, anger and take on the 'life is a jungle' outlook. (Can you already see which drugs will be attractive to which experience types?) And then, sadly, they'll probably end up into some kind(s) of drug(s), and possibly even crime and prison, because the subconscious is so filled with anger, pain, confusion and a need to run from them. It hurts me deeply to see any television documentaries about prison life. These childhood victims, who have since created more victims, are now further being victimized in a torturous setting (this is not to say that people shouldn't be held responsible for their crimes, and this does not include crimes committed out of selfishness). I hope my book can help save some of them. This is why I feel that it's critical how babies and children are treated and what setting they're born into.

So now, given all that tragedy, I'm trying to do something about it in writing this book.

First, let's look at the drug predicament as it is, and try to get some insight into why people take drugs. We'll be looking at the specific drugs also, because different people take different drugs for different reasons.

Initially, people either take drugs out of curiosity, or as a response to pressure or salesmanship from others, because they don't absolutely know what the experience and effects will be like or how they would fit in with their other experiences. But once they know what these effects are, they can consciously choose them when they want. But this is partially an illusion. These initial good effects can't be counted on to show up continuously. If the first time you sit at a blackjack table, you win and have a great feeling, it doesn't mean that that's going to happen every time. And sometimes, you might lose big. One of the things that I want to do in this book is show how to get these (and better) highs naturally and consistently. And this happens by getting rid of what goes on in the subconscious that gets in the way of them just happening naturally. Becoming high naturally is more a process of peeling off layers (like an onion) than adding something on. These layers often are telling us false things that are upsetting us and putting in us the feeling of wanting to seek relief in drugs from these upsets. Or they might be guiding us into thoughts, words and actions that end up creating negative experiences in our life. A person is kind of like an onion with a diamond in the middle. Within yourself you have everything you need to find peace, happiness and satisfaction. You don't need to add anything on. But there's so much garbage on top. We need to settle down, and calm down our quick, impulsiveness to get in touch with the wisdom, radar and discerning abilities that are within. Also we need to focus it on the wisdom of what it needs to reprogram itself to. And every once in a while we may need to release some tension by playing sports, or listening to or playing high-energy music. So now how do drugs affect this situation?

Some drugs make the layers easier to see, and some drugs make them harder to see. But in both cases drugs dull the repercussions that the layers would normally have on our feelings. And voile!, peace, highness and/or happiness is experienced. So then if you like these experiences that result from not having layers, you basically have two choices. Get the layers out of sight by sweeping them under the drug (which is only temporarily possible, as will be discussed in the chapter that talks about 'tolerance'), or get them out of sight by getting rid of them. This example is an example of taking drugs for invironmental reasons.

Taking drugs for environmental reasons would be because a person is in an unnatural environment and is either too lazy, too insecure or too unknowledgeable to change it (which are still, really, invironmental problems). So then they try to use drugs to block out the parts of the environment that are unnatural and that are causing them to experience pain, frustration and anger. The get-more-oblivious drugs 'serve' well here.

Let's look at some more invironmental reasons.

(1)To Run From Guilt

This is the desire to squelch what the conscience, in trying to guide us in the right direction, is trying to say to us. The person, in this case, is *fixed* on *having* to do a certain thing. And because of peer pressure, confusion, fear, greed, laziness, etc., they want to block the con-science's messages and feelings of guilt out.

Also there is unnatural guilt that comes from bad programming by self and others. Later I'll show you how to discern the difference between these two, and program the bad source out.

It would be so nice if everyone realized that there is more wisdom in their natural conscience than they could ever hope to have, and knew how to tap into it. It would save them so much trouble. Also, if people were in tune with their consciences, no one would ever have to be concerned about anyone else because all bad inclinations would be held in check by this 'cosmic policeman'.

Drugs Used: The less-awareness drugs. (The specific drugs that are in this category, and all of the other categories in this chapter, are described in chapter 7. But for now, here's a quick list:

The less-awareness drugs- heroin, alcohol, downers, cigarettes, PCP, opium, qualudes, marijuana and tranquilizers.

The heightened-awareness drugs- LSD, peyote, mescaline, marijuana, hashish and all other psychedelics.

The hyperactive drugs- cocaine, speed, amphetamines,

coffee, sugar and uppers).

(2)A Desire For Realness

This is a rejection of the dishonest, greedy, uptight, insincere, tense, competitive aspect of our world; and a liking of calmness, relaxedness, highness, truth, beauty, nature, religion, etc.. The motive here is excellent, but I want to later show how all of these treasures can be had naturally with education, dealing with the subconscious in a clean up effort, and making changes in thought, word, action and environment.

<u>Drugs Used</u>: The heightened-awareness drugs.

(3)To Run From Emotions

This is an attempt to get rid of an emotion, or emotions, that a person doesn't know how to deal with, is too intense, is deemed as being inappropriate (for their current image and environment), is survival threatening, could possibly cause others' criticism and/or rejection of them, or is detrimental to them being able to manipulate a situation the way that they want it to be. Some of the common emotions here would be: anger, pain, fear, frustration, judgment, shyness and depression. It's unfortunate when a person feels like they have to run from a negative-feeling emotion, such as depression, and try to sweep it under a drug. They just need to realize that nature invented these emotions for a good purpose. And that good purpose is to 'get the person's attention, get them to focus on a certain aspect of their life, and take action to the problem(s) therein'. Running, hiding and suppressing are just the opposite of the emotion's natural purpose. But nature will not release the person from the emotion until the necessary, required work is done. This work could be: education, life-situation-transformation, behavior modification, attitude adjustment, approach-to-living adjustment, increased understanding about the truths of our (and/or this) life, etc.. The proper actions can be discovered through: meditation, reflection, counseling, reading, dwelling, church, logically thinking it out, etc.. A good definition of depression: depression is a negative-feeling emotion whose positive purpose is to forcibly get our attention (by it's pain), get us to focus on an area in our life that needs work, and do that work. A good rule of thumb about depression would be: the only thing that will lift a depression permanently is to force ourselves to take the actions that will solve the problems that are fueling the depression. In other words, if depression's function is to get us to do certain things (not just sit around and suffer), then if we do those things, it will leave, because it no longer has a reason to exist. Depression is a real "effect" that has a real "cause". This "cause" must be discovered either by introspection, reading or conversation. Then the proper action(s) that it requires to be released must be discovered, and then taken. Sometimes depression looks like it might just be a pain reaction to a loss. But this type of depression also falls within our definition, in that, what we need to do is: 'evaluate' every aspect of what caused this loss, and which of our "policies for living" need to be corrected, and how. And the intensity of the depression will be proportional to the importance of the area of life that the loss occurred (or is occurring) in, and also the amount of pain that was caused (or is being caused) to ourself, others, and life in general. Then as this evaluation and correction work is being completed, the depression will proportionally lift. Unfortunately though, instead of doing this work, many times people will try to bury the depression or run from it. But this buried depression will be like a constant thorn in a person's side, and their personality will have to be altered to make room for it. And this buried depression will continually try to resurface and have it's work completed. Therefore it will take constant effort to keep it down. This effort I call a 'drug habit' ('drug' as defined in this book), or continually sweeping-it(in this case, the depression)-under-the-drug. So then why not just take care of it in the first place? I think that most people want to, but 'they' don't know how. 'They' here includes not only themselves, but the media and most of the professional psychology approaches. By the time that you finish reading this book, you'll know how (or at least, you'll know how to know how). The discussion that I've applied here to depression can also be applied to all of the other negative-feeling emotions.

When an emotion becomes too intense, unbearable, and even life threatening, though, psychiatrists have used drugs to calm them down. I feel that the approach taken in this book is sufficient to solve any problem. But I'm not opposed to some drug use, while working under expert supervision, to create a gradual decline in extreme cases. This might prevent some greater harms from happening.

<u>Drugs Used</u>: The less-awareness drugs.

(4)Peer Pressure

A peer group is effective only to the degree that you need or want them. If your needs and wants are fulfilled at home and in other normal relationships within the community, you won't feel needy and be vulnerable to succumbing to a person or a peer group's demands of unnatural behavior from you in order to keep peace and a oneness with them. This can be especially rough at work sometimes because of the wide variety of types of people. So make sure you take this into consideration when choosing a job, where you'll be spending a lot of time being and communicating with others, and where you'll also be under the command of others. You don't want to be forced into a position where you might end up sacrificing your inner peace for a superficial outer peace.

Also, a truly caring parent will fulfill their duty and look out for their children, who are unable to look out for themselves, and do all that they can to put them in a school that doesn't have kids who would harm them physically, emotionally or in their development. There are many private schools available that would be closer to your ideology and would comply with how you want your children to be treated (or not treated), or you can do home schooling or cooperative home schooling, or you can even move.

As far as using parental force against peer pressure, parents can tell their children to say no to drugs, but if the child is not loved and accepted at home in a real way, where their real feelings are respected and taken seriously, the parents have little power or influence. But the peers do have power (unless of course the child rejects both of them and either becomes a loner or semi-succumbs to one or both of them). The peer group can offer a badly needed sense of belonging, love and acceptance and an environment where they can be free to be themselves, and free to discover more about themselves. But where there is real love and support at home, the parents will have importance and credibility and there will be power to say no.

Drugs Used: Any or all of them.

(5)Boredom

Boredom is the sign of a person who has no purpose, direction or discipline and is out of touch with their normal feelings. It is also the sign of a person who is burying their confusion as to how to manifest their time and energy instead of working at trying to resolve it. Or they might be suppressing their normal feelings out of fear or anger. Because drugs will alienate a person from their normal feelings, boredom often comes after pro-longed drug use.

Drugs Used: Any or all of them.

(6)The Something's-Missing Syndrome

I'd like to divide this into two categories. The first category contains the physical needs, e.g. romance, career, dissolving emotional blocks, etc.. The other category contains the spiritual needs. It's been said that there is a God-sized void in us that only God can fill. I've experienced this to be true. Nothing else that I tried to shove in a certain unsatisfied area within me could fill or satisfy it. For now I'll describe this as 'the need to know the truth', i.e. the true answers to the questions about the meaning of this life and it's specifics.

Drugs Used: The heightened-awareness drugs.

(7)To Control The Body's Pace

Basically,tospeedup, s l o w d o w n , and all the degrees in between. No discussion about drugs would be complete without talking about pace. But there is an optimum pace that we should be going at in every instant. And it gives us feedback when we go too slow (antsyness, boredom, frustration), and when we go too fast (fatigue, unconnectedness). A lot of times the reason that people take drugs is to alter their pace. They've got an erroneous fixture in their minds that this is what they need to do. So they become continuously dependent on a drug for what their body is not capable of naturally. But they pay a big price with their health and their current, ongoing life experience. Nothing is worth paying these prices. Hopefully they won't be forced to learn this lesson by having to go through a major health problem, like many have had to. You can always trade your car in, but you've only got one body. And you have to live in it your whole life and experience it's sufferings. Also, permanent damage is permanent. The older people's advice, "...as long as you have your health." , should be listened to. Especially since they are at the age when it's time to start paying the piper for a lifetime of subtle and major physical abuse. Do whatever you have to to release yourself from your mind's unnatural pace expectations. Make a relaxed, natural pace the *constant* and your life's actions the *variable*, rather than the other way around.

Drugs Used: Any or all of them.

(8)Curiosity

An initial encounter with a drug will either turn a person off or lead them to any one of, or a combination of, (1) through (7). But there can also be serious damage with first time use, as with LSD or PCP. I guess a rule here could be: beware of initial encounters with drugs that have initials.

Drugs Used: Any or all of them.

(9)To Get High

To help them get to the 'higher levels of existence' (which also feel better), whether it be a spiritual high (love); or a super-relaxed, laid-back comfort; or a joyful exuberance; or a high-energy excitement; or a left-lobe shutdown, so that they can really be 'outside' of themselves and openly and thoroughly experience what's out there, or openly and thoroughly experience what's inside of themselves without a lot of mental activity or interference that is trying to suppress and blind them to the beautiful and high experiences that are naturally within. The already-programmed mind is constantly vying for their attention. But depending on the quality and the intuneness-with-nature of the existing subconscious programs, the experiences that they cause might be low and/or negative (e.g. tension, anger, frustration or an upset). But all of the above-mentioned high experiences can be had naturally without drugs and without having to deal with the problems of drugs. For example, listening to or playing high-energy music (at the right time and in the right place) can be a very transforming experience. Let me make this very clear: I am not anti-high. As a matter of fact, I am extremely pro-high. I love the higher states more than anything else. But I am such a lover of highness that I don't want to put up with any of the hassles or unsurities of drugs. And I know that all of the high states can be had naturally. It just takes mental work to have them easily and naturally just be in us. And this work is all computer programming work, i.e. (1) adding to: putting ourselves in the places where we will acquire the new information about the higher states that we're supposed to program in, and (2) deleting from: replacing the old low information, conclusions and programs with the new higher ones.

You see, I am not out to *suppress* the drug scene, but rather I am out to *replace* it with a better approach, saying: you can achieve highness in a better way, and not have to deal with the problems that go along with drugs. I mean (and this is one place that the current war on drugs is missing it a little bit), you can't expect people to give up their current highest states or highest approaches to life based on expletives telling them that drugs are bad

37

or that they should say no to them. The only way that you can permanently get a person to give up drugs is to show them something higher that they can replace them with.

Fun

What about those that say that taking drugs is fun? Even though taking drugs might sometimes be experienced by some as being fun, this doesn't mean that taking drugs is a good thing. Just as the possibility of having sex outside of marriage might be perceived by some as potentially being fun, it's really very dangerous and harmful (pregnancy, an _entire_ human life having to start out without a proper nest having been built for it or without a marriage to support it, disease, hurting their spouse, guilt, murder, destroying their marriage, etc.), and is a statement that either their ego, their marriage, their sensitivity to their conscience, or their intuneness with nature is in bad shape and in need of repair. I feel that because sex outside of marriage (and anything that promotes it), committing crimes, and taking drugs so often have such horrendous consequences, that people shouldn't even be allowed the liberty to do these. Not as a restraint on their personal liberty, but as a protection for the victims they may cause (e.g. sex outside of marriage can cause: unwanted children, disease, emotional trauma, etc.; drugs can cause: brain damage, auto accidents, crime, etc.; and crime speaks for itself). I'm trying to persuade people here to make those repairs and have a higher life _naturally_. Not only will the guilt be gone, but there are many positive experiences that will unfold, including 'fun'. And this fun will be real and cause no harm. These positive experiences are the natural rewards for living life in such a way as to not hurt anyone else or self, and for constructively adding to life by living it out in it's higher intended ways. I mean, we can be one of those people who can't sing but say that they can. And who then con and push their way into musical situations (if you haven't experienced this type of situation, I'm sure you can imagine the bad feeling and tension that this would create). Or, we can really be responsible and learn, practice and develop our singing ability and really have something good to add to a musical situation and earn a good feeling (and you know the good feeling that being able to contribute something good creates).

Other examples of things that are considered 'fun' but that really are dangerous: the game "chicken out", in which 2 or more contestants push themselves close to a point of danger and then they see who will come closest to that point before bailing out. Examples of this would be: cars driving up to the edge of a cliff, waiting until the last second to open your parachute, walking through railroad tunnels, two people throwing knives closer and closer to their feet, Russian roulette, etc..

Now I'm not judging, pointing fingers or trying to put pressure on anyone. I realize that for a person to instantly change is not possible, and to try to use condemnation, criticism, belittling, pressure, etc. to get a person to change only has the opposite effect. It either depresses them and lowers their self-esteem, and/or makes them offended, angry, defensive, argumentative and want to rebel. I'm just trying to get people to see if they're living in Death Valley or not, and then show them Hawaii. And then try to persuade them to make the move (with also showing them how to do it). I'm trying to encourage growth, because the feeling of 'fun' can be had in natural ways (e.g. the cuteness of babies, marriage, children, music, art, games, projects, inspired work, community groups, playing sports, being out in nature, etc.) without drugs and without causing any harm. And not only is fun being had for ourselves, but we're helping create it for others too.

The 'Recreational' Drug User

Everyone has to decide how to live this life for themselves, and if drugs are going to be a part of their life or not. I mean, it's hard to tell the recreational drug user that taking drugs is bad and wrong when they say that they're having fun doing so and that it's not hurting them. All that I can do here is tell of my personal experiences, feelings and logic, and try to show how people's lives would *permanently* advance to better states quicker without drugs. Then it's up to each person to very honestly, and in the privacy of their own minds, look into their heart and evaluate what I'm saying for themselves, and if and how they want to apply any of what I'm saying or not. What I can say though is that I've had up and down experiences with drugs, and to the extremes and probably most of the degrees in between. I decided to stop taking them because they could no longer do anything positive for me. Actually, it became very obvious to me that using drugs was an avoidance of the very positive life that nature had carved out for me (and my involvement with the rest of life). Drugs also prevented me from getting to that positive life because they made me insensitive to the messages in my body that are meant to get and keep me there. They made those messages very distant and the picture very foggy. They would just get in the way of me doing the positive things that I needed to do. They just became momentum-killers to the good things that I was trying to accomplish. Times spent in drug use during these days were like 'holes in my life'. We need to respond to, not run from, our negative-feeling emotions. We need to have meditative, reflective times in private to see the positive, necessary things that they are trying to get us to see and do, things that will lead us to a higher life naturally. We need to do the 'work' that it takes to get 'natural highness' rather than try to drug ourselves into artificial euphorias that are just temporary, will once again require more drugs, and will many times have an equal and opposite low that we'll have to experience. Plus, our problems that are keeping us from the natural highs just fester and get worse. Why not just solve them once and for all?

The only times that I found benefit from drugs, was when my life was so 'out there', that the relaxed high from the drugs would help put things back into perspective by showing me how off the track that my life-experience was in comparison to it. Kind of like when you go on vacation, and then come back home, you get a more objective view of your 'normal' life than when you're in it day-to-day. Taking drugs can sometimes be like a spiritual vacation. But there are other natural ways to take spiritual vacations that don't carry with them the problems that drugs carry (e.g. meditation, playing sports, a movie, a tape, listening to a person speak, church, music, etc.). If a person is that 'out there', they need to change their actions so that good experiences are produced instead of bad or mediocre ones. In this book, I show how to eliminate the unnatural actions, and what to transform the energy for them to. I also show ways to experientially be in high states and see how out there we are *without having to take drugs*. So I now feel that for any function, drugs aren't necessary. There are natural ways that better handle any need. Taking drugs is like putting a band-aid on a leaky roof. It sort of does the job for a while, but it's much better to fix it permanently and correctly in the first place, even though it takes a little more effort. Because, in the long run, there will be even more effort required and a lot of unnecessary discomfort in between. And what if a major storm hits? As it's been said: a stitch in time, saves nine. I would imagine though that the reason that most people take the band-aid approach is not because of laziness or irresponsibility, but because they don't know what's really wrong and/or how to fix it (this was my case). After reading this book, they won't have either of these problems. Also, irrespective of the recreational drug user who might want to defend their use of drugs, I do see a lot of people having a hard time with drugs (and/or life) both in the media and on the streets. And some of them do want to change their predicament. These are the people for whom this book is mainly designed and intended.

Parties
You don't need drugs to have a party. Basically, a party is when people get together and have a good time. And usually there's an air of excitement, energy, happiness and fun. We have little parties in our house all the time. And much of it is inspired by our baby. We all just get on his level and have a great time. We chase each other around the house, tickle him, play games with him (like peek-a-boo, who's-that-baby-in-the-mirror, etc.), and just sometimes get happy and excited for no apparent reason. And then when that energy is used up, we're on to a different kind of activity at a lower energy level (e.g. work, eating, reading, taking a nap, going out, etc.),

which also feels natural and is very satisfying, just more relaxed. And a lot of other times when I get together with people it's a party atmosphere (relatives, friends, work, etc.). A party is just people getting together and releasing joy. And all of the drugless parties that I'm involved in are more satisfying than any drug party that I ever went to. Because they are just as energetic and as much fun, but they don't have the cloud, stupor, hangovers, physical and emotional unsurities, and potential craziness (criticism, paranoia, sexual games and pressures, occasional fights, etc.). Some people need to take drugs in order to party because their lives are so filled with unnaturalness that nature won't release the reward of joy to them. If a person feels like they have to take drugs to be open and to get in touch with some semblance of joy so that they can be in a party, they are taking the wrong approach (for all of the physical, emotional, mental, natural, spiritual, affect-on-the-environment and future-considerations reasons that I give throughout the book). They probably need to go through a partyless period in their life and address and resolve what is blocking their joy. And maybe even to a point of being in "divine quarantine" (I had to). This is what monasteries, ashrams, drug rehabilitation centers, caves, etc. are supposed to be all about. Also, following the plan in this book will get a person through this. And when they come out on the other end of this quarantine with the work completed, they'll be good for themselves and all of life, and be able to party drug-free.

Chapter 6
A Searching Person's
Menu Of Choices

Let's take a look at the menu of choices a person has when they're confused about how to approach their drives and/or they have no support base of real love.

So the two commodities being sought here are <u>wisdom</u>, and a <u>support system</u> based on real love.

The highest and most satisfying state of wisdom is the <u>absolute truth</u>. The highest and most satisfying support system is that which is based on <u>real love</u>. This can be their home, church, relatives, friends, co-workers, social group, beliefs, etc..

As far as wisdom goes, there are three possible states that a person can find themselves in.

(1) They are very lucky and stumble onto the *absolute truth*, recognize it, and incorporate it into their lives.

(2) Experiencing a *wisdom void*, which manifests in their emotions as confusion, emptiness, lostness, meaninglessness, etc..

(3) *False wisdom*, i.e. treating what isn't ultimately true as being true. This would also include *low-grade wisdom*, where less than the optimum approach is being taken. I include this in here because truth and untruth are very polar, i.e. something is either true or it isn't. For the true seeker of wisdom, there isn't any in-between.

We all experience all 3 of these, each to a certain percent, and with all 3 percents adding up to 100. This would be a gauge of the *relative truth* of our basic philosophy. What is critical is what the numbers are, and especially the one's that relate to life's main drives (i.e. marriage, job, purpose, how to deal with our inner workings, etc.), because we are indelibly attached to these drives and feel their repercussions. The rule here being that truth yields positive experience, and untruth yields negative experience. (Positive experience can also be extracted from untruth, but not without causing negative experiences in other parts of one's life).

A person who is inclined to sweep-it-under-the-drug is usually experiencing hopelessness, lostness, fear, apathy, laziness, nothingness or confusion as a result of their wisdom voids. Instead of letting these feelings naturally come on and (due to their discomfort) force the person to seek solutions (which is the very nature of their function), they use drugs to try to make themselves oblivious to this natural process. Once again, was nature wrong to invent these feelings? No. They have a very positive purpose. The only problem is knowing how to respond to them. By the time you finish this book, you'll know exactly what to do.

So then why does a person try to squelch this natural process? They want to push away their nagging thoughts and others' arguments about their false wisdoms either because of: confusion about what's right stemming from previous faulty programming; they don't want to threaten their attachments to others who continue to push these false wisdoms; or because their ego won't let them experience 'being wrong'.

As far as all of the possible choices go, the only *real* solution is to 'be at where you're at' (without drugs), and then work to increase your '(1)' percentage {'(1)' being the previously mentioned 'knowledge of the absolute truth'}.

Another choice is the aforementioned drug approach of trying to block the whole dilemma from consciousness. It becomes more and more difficult to solve these problems the longer you take this approach though because, after blocking them out for a long period of time, you start doing it automatically and subconsciously, and you eventually forget that you have these problems. Of course, to varying degrees, this is the state that we're all in. But what I and this book are all about is to continually dig in and clean up. (I'll show you some great digging and cleaning tools as the book progresses).

The only other choice is to wallow in the lostness and

despair. But most people can't stand this too long and usually are driven to one of the other two approaches.

As far as 'support system' goes, there are also 3 possible states a person can find themselves in.

(1) A support system based on real love, whereby the person feels the energy and freedom to follow their natural drives.

(2) A *support void*. i.e. a lack of being tied to others.

(3) A support group where the ties are abused, used for selfish purposes, and the interactions are based on falseness rather than truth.

Once again, we all have a combination of all 3 states, with varying percentages. But where there is false love we will still be left with a gnawing need that only real love can satisfy. On top of this we'll also have nagging convictions pressing on our consciousness trying to inform us of the offness of what we're involved in. We then either listen to the feeling and the convictions and try to change the situation, or we sweep them under the drug. One thing that's sad about today's situation is that people (especially young people) are giving up too easily. They throw in the towel to false living and drug use without much of a fight. But, of course, there has to be an explanation for this. I believe that the explanation lies in what they're being given to fight it with. The media is just one example after another of life-gone-wrong and very little of life-going-right. How can people today have an idea of what *real love* and *naturalness* look and feel like if they never see it? (The hyper- empty-comedy-supported - by - laugh - tracks, heaviness, and violence in today's media aren't manifestations of love.) How can there be any hope to create something that you barely know exists? Compare today's sitcoms with some of the pre-1965 sitcoms. Compare today's cartoons and movies to yesteryears (there was some bad stuff back then, but it was in the minority and not nearly as intense). Most of my generation never even <u>heard</u> of drugs (except alcohol) until after graduation (1965), let alone take them. There wasn't any fear on the streets because there was much less crime. There was an openness and a unity in the nation and in the communities. People today don't have the same advantages of living in these kinds of situations. It's much harder to be normal today than it was then. But it's not impossible.

Many people today appear to be spiritually lazy, just going along with the crowd, imitating role models of falseness, showing up for work and going through the motions of their job, and then just plopping themselves in front of their T.V. absorbing whatever happens to be on. Of course, we all have our different specialized function in life and we shouldn't have to be concerned about all of this. People should be able to just walk in a restaurant and order and not have to get involved in the cooking or menu planning. They've got their own job. They should just worry about doing their job well and be able to trust that the cook and menu planner are doing their jobs well. Well that's my job. To be concerned that what the cook and menu planner are putting out is of a high quality, and to make it easy for people to be spiritually in tune and aligned. And I see the media and the media-makers as being very faulty, greedy and irresponsible towards the emotional and spiritual needs of this country. It's been a snowball effect towards hell since the 1950's. And the carrot that's been leading this goat is greed.

Another sad situation is the person who never made it out of imprinting and just attaches to someone(s) and gives their love indiscriminately (usually tyrants are at-tracted to them {who are also imprints of other tyrants}). Then their life becomes like a pinball, being thrown around through one unreal situation after another, with some normalcy thrown in to keep it afloat. I'm not trying to give the impression that you don't attach to situations, because that's one of the aspects of love. But you don't put on the blinders and do it. That would be not loving yourself.

The solution here is to recognize your need for others and their need for you, to take responsibility for your life, and to pick a support group based on real love (both ways). I'll get specific as to how to do this later in the book. The real problems here are (1) being able to discern real love, and (2) being capable of real love yourself. But have no fear. There are definite rules. And once learned, the real feeling will unlock and flow and be recognized in others. I'll get into these rules later.

Is There A Brotherhood Amongst Drug Users?

In a sense there is, although drug use can be a very lonely endeavor. 'Misery loves company' is one basis for this. Also 'birds of a feather flock together'. The feather in this case is the unspoken philosophy that natural life is not enough and that the only way to enjoyably make it through is with drugs. The fellow drug user, at times, is even seen to be much wiser than the world because of being able to see through the world's folly and not totally succumb to it (the folly that I'm speaking of here is the previously mentioned *plastic*ness. Although drug users have their own brand of folly, which I have partially mentioned at the beginning of this paragraph, and will continue to mention throughout this book). And, in a sense, they're right. Drug users who use depressant-type drugs know that when they're on drugs they generally feel more natural, less impulsive, and able to 'see' more clearly. What I'm trying to do here though is bring them all the way to 'natural', where they won't even need drugs to have these high experiences.

Pride is sometimes attempted in this brotherhood. They pride themselves for rebelling against the world's plasticness and offness. But this pride is false because they have many offnesses themselves of different kinds. The Bible says "why do you look at the speck that is in your brother's eye, but do not notice the log that is in your own eye?". They need to continue to rebel against all offness, and work towards 'naturalness' and 'perfection'. Pride is a pacifying stumbling block to this endeavor.

Occasionally there is an attempt to give an identity to their enemy, which they see as the 'world's cruelty'. Ronald Reagan is a popular focus for this. The irrational feeling is put out that he is to be blamed for all of the evils in this life. The truth is though, that Ronald Reagan is just another person, and actually, one who is making a lot of personal sacrifice to try to do some good in this world. He has put himself on the line both physically and emotionally. He is taking some responsibility for the national and international problems and trying to do something about them, while all that many others can do (who many times are just meandering around in the fog of their own psychodrama), is merely point fingers, instead of offering full, alternative solutions to this country's (and the world's) very complex problems. I see much too much finger pointing and much too little solution offering. (They say that when you point a finger at someone, 3 fingers are pointing back at you. Do it with your hand and see). But isn't this what most political campaigns are? That is, finger pointing and promised results, but no bridges on how to get there. A lot of empty general promises, but very few detailed visions. "We have seen the enemy, and the enemy is us". We each have so much personal and outer positive work in front of us that there is little use in labelling any enemies.

So then, how influential is this brotherhood? Here are some alarming statistics from government surveys and from surveys done by the national publication "Weekly Reader".

(1) 1/4 of all 4th graders feel pressure to take drugs.

(2) 50% of all 7th graders feel pressure to take drugs.

(3) At least 17% of the country's high school seniors have used cocaine.

(4) 57% of those who call cocaine hotlines for help admit they bought their coke at school.

These statistics are even more alarming when you consider that they are talking about a national average. Can you imagine what the numbers would be for New York City, Los Angeles, Chicago and San Francisco?

Is this brotherhood's influence increasing in power? Consider this staggering comparison. Like I said, I graduated from high school in 1965 in San Francisco (a very liberal city). Not only did hardly any teenagers take drugs (outside of an occasional beer on an occasional weekend), but I don't think that hardly any of them had even heard of drugs yet or could name any of them. Our main focuses were the upcoming holidays and events and preparing for them with excitement, e.g. Christmas,

Easter, Halloween, parties, proms, dances, games, etc..

I hope that one day again kids will have these options and the air of happiness that existed then. But for this to happen: drugs would have to be eliminated; sexual morals would have to be reversed to where virginity, going steady and romance were the norm (and not the exception). Also love, family, community and religious values would have to be restored. What do you think? Does it sound like too big a job? Well anyway, in this book I'm just going to focus on *personal* peace and happiness and see if I can help others achieve that. I know, at least, that that is possible.

Chapter 7
Some Physiological Realities

I could get into describing all of the specifics of how all of the drugs react on all of the body systems (circulatory, nervous, respiratory, digestive, etc.), but there are a few good books out that already do this, for those who are interested. But I did want to use this chapter to describe some of the physical realities and overviews of drug use. Those that would be pertinent to the concept of this book are those that would show how drugs *themselves* end up creating problems (overdose, withdrawal, addiction, tolerance, distortion of reality, etc.) that are detrimental to health (physical, mental and emotional), and even life threatening. The drug user needs to be able to tell the difference between *real* body and mind cravings, and *drug-induced* cravings. Because the latter can be eliminated, while the former must be properly responded to. In dealing with any physical problem, it's nice to know how long you have to wait before you can expect results, and what physical side effects must be endured. The specific withdrawal approaches will be dealt with in chapter 19, but for now I want to give a basic overall physiological picture of drugs.

Viewing the whole menu of drugs from an *awareness* viewpoint, I see them falling into 3 categories.

(1) The Get-More-Oblivious Drugs (i.e. less aware)
Heroin, alcohol, downers, cigarettes, PCP, opium, qualudes, marijuana and tranquilizers.
(2) The Heightened Awareness Drugs
LSD, peyote, mescaline, marijuana, hashish and all other psychedelics.
(3) The Hyperactive Drugs (no effect on awareness other than to speed up the process.)
Cocaine, amphetamines, coffee, sugar and other uppers.

I'm going to let my discussion about LSD explain why I'm seeing things in terms of an awareness factor, and why I think that this factor is a key to why people take drugs. Then I'll continue on with a discussion of some of the specific drugs.

LSD: Awareness.Gate Russian Roulette

It is said that we are 90% subconscious and 10% conscious. We pick up on everything around us, but we have 'awareness gates' that only let selected material through to our consciousness. These gates keep out visions and information that are unimportant or meaningless to us, as well as what would cause us pain, shock, repulsion, etc., e.g. seeing a dead animal on the road, someone being hit by a car, etc.. Also they keep out information that we are not ready to assimilate because we haven't taken in mandatory prerequisite information. (The way you can prove this last one to yourself is when you're reading something and you come to something that you don't really understand but you continue reading on anyway. Notice how your mind seems to shut off although it still is saying the sounds of the words in your head. It's still stuck on the last phrase trying to get you to go back and understand it before you move on). This not only works for outer stimuli, but inner stimuli as well, e.g. painful memories (have you ever noticed how pleasant memories just pop into your mind while painful ones rarely do?), realizations about ourselves that would seriously drop our self-esteem, excessive physical pain (even to the point where nothing is let in to our conscious awareness and we pass out), etc.. There are some drugs that we can take to block awareness of pain for a good purpose, e.g. anesthesia in an operation, or for a bad purpose, e.g. cortisone to an athlete's foot so that he can continue to perform, but then he suffers severe damage because he wasn't sensitive to the pain warnings in his foot. With LSD you're playing ' awareness gate Russian roulette ' because LSD will, without the normal sensitivity to what should and should not be allowed into consciousness, break down these gates and allow visions and data to come gushing through that the gates would normally want to keep out. Data that a person's mental structure isn't ready to handle, assimilate and cross-reference with all of the other data and concepts that are in the brain yet (though it may someday). Possibly the reason for this is because with every new bit of information we get, we have to allow it to transform all the data in the brain that it is relevant to. This is why you get a headache when you study or read. Your brain has reached the overwhelm point in being able to assimilate new data and put it together to see the larger overall concepts. Specifically, the norepinephrine, which is the chemical in the brain that carries the electrical charges that transmit data, dries up. So 'blowing your mind ' might be literal and analogous to blowing a computer when you give it too much data for it to handle at once. The Russian roulette aspect comes in because you can't predict what's going to happen. One night you might all of a sudden realize the beauty and nature of real love, or the existence and the nature of the power that authored and created this life and universe. While on another night you might experience that you are trapped in a body, or see the extreme ugliness of the phoniness of those around you. And you might see it so strongly that you won't be able to hide or handle it. A big problem here is: once you've seen what you've seen, even after you come down from the drug, the visions take years to go away (although their intensity gradually decreases), and you must work very hard to incorporate what your mind wasn't ready for yet in order to protect your sanity. So therefore, even seeing something beautiful might be harmful, in the sense that when you come down, you might feel very inadequate in relationship to it. Whereas, the normal route would be: see a little, change a little, feel a little better; see a little more, change a little more, feel even better; etc.,etc.,etc..

Cocaine: More Than Just A Stimulant

(Webster's Dictionary)
-caine: synthetic, alkaloid, anesthetic.

coCAINE, like novaCAINE, is an anesthetic (numbing agent). When taken up through the nose and into the sinus area, It passes through a thin membrane and numbs the frontal lobe of the brain. This is also the same area of the brain where 'frontal lobotomies' are performed (so coke addicts, why not save yourself a lot of drug money and just get a lobotomy { just joking }). This numbing performs a similar function to that of a lobotomy in that it blocks the ability to "feel and respond to (from Webster's definition of 'anesthetic')" disturbing messages from the subconscious. This could possibly account for the paranoia during comedown i.e. the emotion from the surge of suppressed, subconscious disturbing messages.

Personally I think that this is a dumb drug and I don't understand it's popularity. You pay the most for it and yet it's the least pleasurable high, even compared to the inexpensive drugs such as alcohol and marijuana. It's probably more for the 'fad' reason than for any other.

Cigarettes: Mini Heroin

You probably wonder why I include something as mild as cigarettes in this chapter, let alone associate it with heroin. I associate it with heroin because the feeling is the same (as I'll describe below) but just on a much, much smaller level of intensity. And I didn't put it in the 'minor drugs' chapter (8) because the minor drugs chapter is just going to be for non-physically addictive, less obvious drugs that are used as psychological rugs (to have stuff swept under).

For years I smoked 2 packs a day. But then a bed-ridden week with the Hong Kong flu wouldn't allow me to smoke at all. By the time that I got well, I had gathered enough momentum to help me to quit. So I did. Of course, I was plagued with the usual dreams for 6 months that I had started again, only to wake up in relief that I really hadn't. One time years later I had accidentally taken a drag off of a cigarette (thinking that it was a marijuana cocktail) and I could observe a slow wave of numbness coming over my head, body and limbs. It slowly went down my arms, then into my legs, and then into my head. At this time I truly realized that cigarettes were a get-more-oblivious drug. The reason that regular smokers don't experience this numbness coming over them is because they are in a continually numb state. They smoke to keep the numbness from abating.

Marijuana: You Lose A Lot More Than You *Think*

A friend of mine used to smoke marijuana every day and for every occasion (like going to the movies, going to a park, eating, playing sports, watching T.V., eating, listening to some records, waking up, eating....anyway, you get the idea). He did this for a number of years. Finally he started thinking that maybe he was just involved in an empty habit, so he decided to quit and see what that was like. Within the next month after quitting, I got more phone calls from him than I had gotten in the previous 2 years. And in each one he was really excited about a new-found interest in computers and electronics. Also he was getting new ideas for expanding his business and a new enthusiasm and energy to carry them out.

And each good experience, while straight, is recorded as a success. And each success builds a momentum that dope would only interrupt. And actually, anyone can be successful if they want to be. There are opportunities all over the place for everyone. But you have to work for them. And when you're stoned you don't like to work. But nature has provided a high and a satisfaction for when we do inspired work. But you have to stay in touch with the analytical side of your brain and your business energy, and not drug them away to where they are not there for you to be able to use. Grass will drug them away. Also, this business and analytical energy is what helps you solve your personal problems. Another good piece of advice here is: don't be stubborn and pursue something that is not going to bring, or lead you to, financial and emotional success. The repeated failures may drive you back to drugs.

I can relate to his experience from my own personal experience. Maybe I would have an idea in mind for something I could do to further my business, but as soon as I'd get stoned, the feeling to do it would be gone and I'd say "I don't want to deal with straight, uptight, hyper people. They'd probably see that I was stoned anyway. Plus I might not be able to concentrate on what I was saying. And maybe I'd even start laughing because it's all such a joke. Who needs all of that. No, I'm just going to go to the park and play frisbee, or go get more stoned with one of my stoned friends. Actually, now I don't even have that much energy. I can't decide what to do (laughter). I think I'll just relax and stay home and play my guitar and have something sweet to eat".

It's not that the business drive is unreal (although many approach it in an unreal way), It's just that I had numbed mine away and so therefore I couldn't relate to someone else on a level and with an energy that I didn't have available to me.The point that I'm trying to make here is that when you follow your business drive in a humble, natural way, It's a high in itself. Also, you do good for others, you pull your weight, you feel satisfied, and you have the money that you need.

The reason that I put marijuana in both the less-awareness and heightened-awareness categories is because it does seem to do both. This is probably due to the fact that grass makes a person more relaxed and less aware of their problems, which are two ingredients for a higher state. Of course, it also makes us less aware of how to function as a human being. A friend of mine once said that they would often be stoned, walk into a room, and then find themselves thinking "I know that I came into this room for a reason, but I can't remember what it is?"

Sugar

Just as cigarettes are a low intensity example of heroin, sugar is a low intensity example of stimulants. The physical reality is that when you eat things that contain the commercial, highly concentrated forms of sugar (which are at a much higher concentration than your body is designed to easily assimilate), your blood sugar level shoots up above normal and you get an energy rush. The body then reacts to return the blood sugar level by releasing insulin into the blood stream. This lowers the blood sugar level, but it shoots it below normal and you experience a headache and fatigue. Then in your desire to get rid of these, you eat more sugar, which again shoots your blood sugar level above normal. Then more insulin; more headache; more sugar; more sugar rush; etc.,etc.. A side-bummer to all of this is that while this is going on, you keep gaining weight and then your blood pressure goes up. Sugar is a very subtle, yet very evil and powerful drug. It's power lies in the fact that it creeps up on you. It's destruction is slow and gradual, and it robs you of your health, lowers the quality of your general feeling and energy, and ends your life sooner than it would have ended.

What Goes Up Must Come Down

In the rest of this chapter, I want to complete my discussion of physical factors that relate to drugs.

Taking any drug for the first time usually is a shock to our body. There used to be a great commercial on television of a young boy who snuck into the bathroom, lit up his first cigarette and started coughing uncontrollably. Then in the middle of a cough, the film would freeze and an overlay would say: " Don't you think his body was trying to tell him something ? " Well, this is also true for most other drugs. The throwing up with heroin, alcohol, and sometimes even grass; the bitter taste of coffee that must be masqueraded with sugar and cream; the horrible taste of any form of alcohol; the coughing with cigarettes; the shakes and downer comedown with cocaine; etc., etc.. But the body will tolerate chemicals that are detrimental to it's health. I mean, at the two are extremes are *health*, and *death by poisoning*. But there is a huge unhealthful area in between in which negative, painful feedback is given to our consciousness by the body to warn against putting into the body what's being put in, because of it's negative effect on the normal functioning of the body and/or it's parts. This is the primary function of the senses such as taste and smell, and internal feelings such as headaches and emotions. The body also has a way of getting rid of anything bad for it immediately, such as by coughing or vomiting. But if the ego still persists in wanting to put unhealthful substances into the body, the body will start to adjust and work with it in order to lessen the initial shock and to cause the least amount of stress on the system overall. A simple illustration of this is how the digestive chemicals and enzymes are in the mouth and stomach in anticipation of the basic kinds of foods we eat. They tend to make us crave the same basic foods over and over because new foods would mean that they would have to change. Anyone who has gone through sugar withdrawal will tell you how much sweeter fruit tastes now, and how anything with sugar in it is way too sweet and repulsive. Whereas, when they were on sugar, sugar tasted normal and fruit was too bland.

Developing A Tolerance

As the body makes these adjustments (in which the cells actually change) to lessen the unpleasant effects of the drugs, they also lessen the pleasant effects. So to experience the same intensity of the desired effects (e.g. light-headedness obliviousness, energy, relaxedness, insight, highness, etc.), greater doses are needed as the body becomes more tolerant.

Once a person decides that it doesn't want to heed the body's warnings, the body will then readjust as best it can to the new intruder. It will adjust to whatever is put in it, and change it's basic chemical operation in anticipation of the new intruder being put in on a routine basis in order to dull it's effect. But when you put bad things in, there will be bad physical repercussions, such as, a person who mainly eats foods with a high fat content will have a body with a high percentage of fat; a person who mainly eats sweets will have a body with a highly fluctuating blood sugar level. These aren't healthy states though, and although the body will adjust, it will not be able to maintain it's optimum functioning. Where there is change in the input, there will also be change in the output.

The fact that the body is a very groove oriented mechanism, presents further problems in that these grooves have a momentum to them. That is, when you apply the brakes they don't immediately stop. It's more like driving down a street going 70 mph, wanting to make a left turn, and waiting until you're 10 feet before the intersection to apply the brakes. You skid through the intersection and, more than likely, crash into a bunch of things on the other side. Then you come to a stop, go back to the intersection, and go down the street that you originally intended to. This is an illustration of momentum. When the body is in a certain groove (routine), it expects certain types of chemicals, and it expects them regularly. To break the routine means that there must be a withdrawal period, where the body must adjust to new chemicals with new digestive chemicals of it's own, and eliminate the chemical setup that it had when it had adjusted to the unhealthy chemicals. The more powerful the chemicals and the longer the addiction, the more violent the withdrawal. But, at least, it's somewhat comforting to know that the feelings being felt aren't permanent and ones that should cause a person to throw in the towel. But rather, they are temporary and the result of the drug addiction's momentum.

The Wanting.To.Avoid.The.Pain.Of.Withdrawal Syndrome

If a person wants to stop using a drug after much use there's a double-edged sword that they have to deal with. They want to stop the drug because it's no longer getting them high (and/or it's creating a number of miseries on it's own), yet when they feel the withdrawal symptoms coming on, they want to do anything to stop them.

An emotional-time-lapse microcosm of this syndrome that I experienced in one night was when I was over a coke dealer's house. There were four of us sitting around a table doing coke that he was freely giving. And there was an unlimited supply. We just kept passing around the lines while we were talking. And the talking got faster and faster and more intense. It was like being a deflating balloon with words being the air. After a while they had no meaning and no one even knew what they were saying, but we had a compulsion to keep forcing them out. This kept on for hours until each new line started becoming painful. So we'd stop. But then the shakes would start to come on, and they were intensely aggravating, so we'd take another line to put them off. But then that would be painful, so we'd stop. Get the picture?: shakes; intense aggravation; snort; pain; etc., etc.. But all of it was becoming increasingly more unpleasant, and finally there was the realization that we'd have to stop eventually and face the shakes. We all went to bed (I got the couch), but there was no way that sleep was even possible. So I just lay there and the shakes became more and more intense, as did the teeth chattering, and the overwhelming feeling of paranoia. Paranoid of what, I didn't know. My eyes also felt like they were going to pop out. Finally after laying there for a while, the paranoia overcame me and I snuck out because I was even paranoid of the people in the house (is this a joke or what?). I felt like I'd never be able to see these people again (although I did and it was fine. It was all drug induced paranoia). By this time, the sun was up and I just spent the rest of the day with a horrible headache trying to come down. During the comedown my nose and the frontal lobes of my brain ached and felt like a tooth, and it's surrounding area, does when novacaine wears off.

Speaking of teeth, be careful when you take codeine after having wisdom teeth pulled (or any operation for that matter). It kills the pain, but it took me 3 weeks and 3 bottles worth to face up to those shakes.

A theatrical metaphor for the what-goes-up-must-come-down process is the selling-your-soul-to-the-devil-for-a-life-of-fun-now theme.

Another way of putting it would be: when you *steal* euphoria (because it didn't come naturally due to you earning it), you have to pay for your crime. And with drugs, you always get caught because the policeman is built-in within you. With this book I'm trying to say that in the long run it's so much better to have taken the natural route.

I remember how naive I felt when I was going through all of this. I would just jump at whatever looked the best. And I would look up to other people and trust them. I didn't really know if they had wisdom or not, but looking back I can see that I just blindly acted and felt as if they did. I guess that's because that that's the way it should naturally be (i.e. trusting our elders for wisdom as to how to live life). But since then, I've learned that if you want to avoid the pitfalls of life, there is no room for spiritual laziness. One of the functions of this book is to show a person how to find the answers for living life themselves.

Chapter 8
The Minor Drugs

As I have stated before, there is a process and a formula in a person taking the sweeping-it-under-the-drug approach to life. And, although I initially set out to write this book to help the major-drug user and those who want to help them, I discovered that this formula and process could also help explain other behavior problems in life, which I will call 'minor drug' use (and abuse).

Recapping the process: sweeping-it-under-the-drug is a process by which a person uses something (herein called a drug) to alter aspects of their current state or condition by blocking their ability to be in touch with the feedback that their conscience, sense of logic and intuition are trying to give them through their mind and feelings. Various drugs are used to avoid these messages that are pushing on their consciousness. Messages that want the person to take action to restore certain areas of their life to normalcy. The person who chooses the sweeping-it-under-the-drug approach doesn't feel that they can handle or adequately respond to this feedback, or they don't want to deal with it in the present. This can be for a number of reasons, some of which are: laziness, fear of being overwhelmed by painful emotion, not being able to work 'questioning' into their present life circumstances, not wanting people to see that they are suffering, hoping it will go away, a threat to their image, feeling like there's nothing that they can do about it, etc..

Now when these messages are being blocked out, the body sometimes responds with a euphoria, as it would if they didn't exist. But it's a 'stolen euphoria', not an earned one. And the reason that a person feels the need to steal it is due to a lack of their lives and their personalities being in tune with nature. An intuneness that would create the euphoria that they're trying to steal. This becomes a major problem when the person decides to try to depend on the drug for the euphoria. Really though, this is a slap in the face to nature. But nature will have it's say by creating some very noneuphoric problems for the person taking this approach. The only real approach is to have patience, continually stay in touch with the problems pushing on our consciousness, and solve them as they come up (also simultaneously cleaning up the backlog of problems that have been avoided).

Some people might agree with the idea that *continued* drug use is bad, but they would argue that occasional use is good because it lets us know what the highs of life feel like, how great they are, and how inadequate our lives are in comparison. And that these visions of the highs will inspire us to do whatever we have to do to naturally create them. But I would disagree with this argument for the following reasons. First of all, I don't see many people propelled to growth anymore from this type of drug inspiration. I see them mostly propelled by the emotional pressure from the mental, emotional and lifestyle problems that they're using drugs to run from. Most people who use drugs use them to keep putting off their problems rather than face them. They don't just dip in and dip out. They have an unreal picture of themselves and their life, and they are more inclined to try to steal euphoria than create it naturally. Secondly, seeing themselves in a high state may inspire a person to want to be there but do they have the patience and the strength to work their way up naturally, or will they just want to be lazy and rely on the drug until the drug itself eventually forces them to stop taking it? But many never make it to this end point without experiencing addiction, permanent mental and/or physical damage, loss of relationships, loss of job, poverty, death, etc.. Thirdly, there's the danger factor. Taking LSD, for example, truly is the same as Russian roulette. For the good that I got out of it, I paid a far, far greater toll in pain and damage. Had I to do it over again, I never would have taken any drug. What do they say: ignorance is bliss? I would agree, in the sense that we should only have knowledge that we are able to comprehend in a natural state. I may have gained some insight and wisdom, but I've suffered much greater losses on the mental and emotional levels. I feel that if I would have just taken the natural route, my life would have been much, much better.

On less intense, relaxation and insight drugs like alcohol and marijuana, the danger lies in the decisions that might be made in a non-reality state, e.g. to try other drugs that would be more dangerous, to continue use of the current drug and avoid one's *real* life, to not see a red light while driving, etc..

Taking a drug approach to the problem-messages (e.g. pain, emptiness, guilt, longing, confusion, dwelling, etc.) also isn't good for the following reason: if there's a bee in the room and we cover our eyes and ears, **it doesn't go away**. It's still there and can potentially sting us, but now we're not in a position to protect ourselves from it.

Besides, my testimony is: if you continue to take the natural route, you'll eventually come to the point where *any* drug experience will be a downer and an intrusion.

The fact that the 'recreational drug-user' *feels* inspired to take drugs (although I do feel that a good percent of recreational drug use is mentally forced and based on hope, or out of laziness or ignorance of not knowing what better to do) is an indication that their life is in a lowered state. That is, if they see a drugged state as one that they want to be in, then it must be higher than the one that they are in just before they choose it. And most of them are unaware of their condition, as they go through life trying to maintain the 'everything is fine' facade, even to themselves. What I'm trying to offer here is an alternative to this 'living in unrealness', because the fruit of unrealness is a dull ache and a wall that all of the the positive feelings of life can't completely penetrate, but the negative feelings of life can and do bounce back off of this wall. This is the condition that drugs are being used to combat. But, for all of the reasons that I've been continuously giving, drugs aren't a solution to this dilemma. But slowly eliminating unrealness, and slowly taking on realness is. I would also like to address here an approach to life that most people who use drugs (to any degree) take. And that is: just survive from day to day, and when messages of stress, pain, anger, emptiness, etc.

come in, use drugs to slip into oblivion until sleep happens, and then start all over again the next day. But there is a much higher, more fulfilling experience to be had. The whole point of this book is to show the reader that this is the case, and also to show how to make the transition to it. We don't have to try to be satisfied with the mundane existence that modern society may have carved out for us, or that we just find ourselves in. Actually, I don't think that it's possible to be satisfied with it. That's why drugs are so popular. Many weren't designed to live the way that they are living and now they're trying to use chemicals to help them accept these unnatural lifestyles. In this book I'm trying to show how we were designed to live, and get the reader to see that their intuition is in agreement with this. And this natural lifestyle is a lifestyle where drugs aren't needed. So now how is a person to achieve this natural lifestyle? Take a step back, objectively look at what you are doing in this life, try to see the higher, natural lifestyle (which will be shown how to do in this book), decide that that is what you want, learn how to make it happen (which this book will also show), and then start constructing this new, higher life. One of the beauties about this natural lifestyle is that it is available to every single one of us. We are all equal, and we all have our (pre-designed and pre-determined) niche. Our actions will all manifest differently (specialization, ala the ants), but we all have access to the same degree of rewards, which are: love, peace, happiness, satisfaction, fulfillment, etc.. The best things in life aren't things. And the funny thing, as we struggle and strive, is that we just need to surrender and gently fall back into the experience, rather than run after it.

If we really want to solve the drug problem in this world, what we have to do is make this world a place where people don't have so many problems in trying to satisfy life's most basic requirements, i.e. job, family, money, etc.. Because if a natural life is made too difficult to achieve, this can discourage and weaken a person and make them just want to throw in the towel to drugs.

Recapping the formula: We can use drugs to push our problems out of view at first, but they will then push harder to be seen, which will then require more drugs, etc., etc.. In other words, it's a losing battle. So inevitably we must deal with the problems. Plus, times spent in drug use are like big, gaping holes in our lives. I know that it's easy to get cynical in this life, but nature really does have many wonderful experiences for us to have if we just follow it's way. And all that means is to be natural and naturally deal with problems as they come up. And with this book I'm trying to show how to do that.

Now this process and formula can happen on a more subtle, less dramatic level (the minor drugs), but still rob us of the fullness of life and feeling that we can experience by being real, clean and in-tune.

For example: someone in our life might be causing us grief, pain, aggravation, etc.. But instead of taking self-protective action by nicely communicating with them (or breaking off relations if they don't care enough to engage in this natural approach to normalizing the relationship), we might opt to grin and bear it, and then watch boxing matches and root for one boxer to punish the other. Or we might be addicted to sad movies and cry and identify with the victims (the drug approach). What we're doing here is sweeping the anger and pain under the drug (sports and movies) and using these mediums to try to let the emotion fizzle out. This probably wouldn't be so bad if a person was *reflecting* on their reactions to these particular events on television, in an attempt to better understand the contents of their subconscious, or their present circumstances which they're trying to clean up. But for many this is a *continual* approach to life. But what a tense, turbulent, unpeaceful, unhappy, empty, saccharin approach. Plus it's about as effective as scratching a growing rash on the skin. It may slightly relieve the immediate itch, but it doesn't get rid of the problem or alleviate the growth of the dilemma. In other words, it just gives a semi-illusion of relief. The real solution is to deal with people nicely, but honestly and directly, and eliminate from your life those who can't treat you nicely in return.

I talked in Chapter 6 about awareness-gates that the subconscious mind uses to keep things from consciousness that are either useless to a person, or that a person is not ready to handle. Well a person can set up another layer of artificial gates and develop their own gate regimen with *compulsive activity* such as television, music, magazines, sports, eating, clubs, shopping, etc.. But this whole process is *ultimately* unnecessary, because the problems being run from are *solvable,* even though it may not always feel like they are (in which case only 2 alternatives are left: sweeping them under a drug, or suffering). Usually fears of harm, loss, failure and rejection are what keep people from living a full life and keeps them sweeping things under these minor drugs. Also giving up the responsibility of their lives and placing themselves under the thumbs of others who'd give unnatural guidelines for their behavior. But in the final analysis, the real problem is : not knowing how to solve the problems. Hopefully, after reading this book they will.

The solutions to the minor drug dilemmas are the same as with the major drugs. What's needed is a deep and thorough understanding of the truth, an ability to flow with the natural self, and an ability to *restrain* the unreal thoughts and inclinations, and *retrain* them by educating ourselves with the truth. Then when you're living out your natural energy as intended, you'll be so busily involved in satisfying activities, that you wouldn't let any drug, major or minor, intrude. Also very important is an ability to create healthy environments and a healthy invironment. This can be done by making any necessary changes in the present ones, or eliminating the unhealthy ones and creating new healthy ones. (which I'll fully talk about how to do in later chapters). The invironment, though, is critically important. Because many times it finds fault in the environment and tries to change it, when the fault and the cause of upset really lies within itself. The invironment is not *truly* seeing the environment. So therefore, the invironmental perceptions and approaches are what need to be changed, not the environment. A landlady that I once had made a great statement to me one time as I was heading off to Europe (an attempt at environmental change) expecting to find the promised land. She said "just remember: after your long journey, when you get off of the plane, you are going to be there".

So now, what are some of these minor drugs that we opt for (instead of facing, understanding and dealing with our real feelings), and how do they work?

(1) **Food** - In the process of writing this book, and carefully examining the sweeping - it - under - the - drug process, I started to see that I had two non-chemical drug habits that also could be described in terms of this process. And those were: food and sports.

With food I observed that I had the following compulsive routine.

My conscious or subconscious mind would say: "go to the refrigerator.......now open the door.......now stand there and decide on something to eat". But then I would say: "none of this looks appealing. And I'm not even hungry anyway". But then my mind would reply: "I don't care. Pick something out anyway. And make sure you don't leave one thing on your plate!"

This was my way of dealing with 'being filled with and pressured by mysterious, confusing feelings' rather than stopping and investigating what these feelings might be, and how I could normally resolve them. But, like all drugs, it would only work for a short time. I'd still end up feeling pressured or feeling bad, but now I'd also have to feel the pain of an over-full stomach. I definitely wasn't acting in sync with myself. This approach was about as effective as answering a baby's cries with beer (unfortunately I've heard of people doing this). They can hush the baby for a while by making it full and numb and dizzy, but they still haven't solved the baby's need (nutritional, diaper change, holding, burping, attention, etc.).

I took this food-as-a-drug approach for a few years rather than face the fact that I was overwhelming my life with activity (and much of it turned out to be the wrong activity). Instead of listening to the inner feedback that was trying to tell me which actions were and were not important and necessary, I'd stubbornly bludgeon ahead with my own plans and demands of my mind and body. As a result, there were many times where I would be pained and drained. And in these times of stress and energy-drain I'd eat. I also used to eat out of boredom. In those few years I gained 100 pounds. So now as a result of the health problems the new weight created, I'm no stranger to diets. (Actually I've been dieting most of my adult life to counteract this drug tendency). I've tried all of them. But in the process of writing this book, I've completely resolved this life-long problem. I'd like to pass on the diet that I'm on now because it's the only one that has worked in a lasting-healthy-painless way (coincidentally this is the one that doctor's have been recommending for years).

(1) <u>1200 calories per day</u> of eating exactly what you crave. But try to stay away from any heavily-processed or drug food such as sugar and alcohol. As far as balanced nutrition goes, I wouldn't worry about 'getting all 4 of the basic food groups each day'. The body has a way of getting all of the nutrition that it needs over the long haul by what it makes you crave. (The number of calories will vary according to sex, age, size and amount of physical activity).

(2) <u>Regular moderate exercise</u> (don't kill yourself. Listen to your body's feedback as to how much it can take).

(3) <u>Patience</u> that the weight will eventually be gone. But in order not to create any health risks or suffer too much, you'll have to let it go slowly (1 to 2 pounds a week on the average). Keep a journal of your daily weight. It will encourage you to see the loss and how it happens (i.e. surges, plateaus, rate, etc.).

(4) <u>Resolving the sweeping - it - under - the - drug aspect of eating.</u> This can be done by applying the suggestions of this book. If you don't deal with the *cause*, you're going to have the same *effect* (or transfer it to another drug).

Since realizing all of this and applying it, I've lost 35.5 pounds at an average of about 2 pounds per week <u>without any hunger or discomfort</u>. And that is because this is really the natural way to eat. And I know that I can <u>easily</u> keep this up until all of the weight is off. If my body gives me the message to go over the 1200 calorie limit every once in a while, I will. Because I want to stay in tune with it's health-maintaining messages. (But I end up marking these calories into the next day's budget and I always end up making them up within a couple of days). I trust it's feedback for that within it's operations that I can't see and that I don't understand (and in many cases, that even medical science doesn't understand). But I know that I'll eventually lose it all. Maybe just not at an aggressive put-on-the-blinders-and-ignore-the-rest-of-my-health pace. And I am enjoying the results of losing the weight: the way my clothes fit, a healthier feeling, the way I look, more energy, more stamina, etc..

But a plan to achieve and maintain a normal weight won't be successful unless you resolve or sublimate the drug aspect of eating. The drug addict's first inclination in choosing a diet is to go for one of the fad diets that say you can 'eat all that you want', (even though it may be of just one particular kind of food, e.g. protein or fruit or celery), i.e. keep the addiction of being able to nervously and compulsively eat, and still lose the weight. Fat chance. Literally. They can lose weight with these, but there is a high pain and hunger factor, and a damage to health risk. And they create such a nutritional imbalance that they end up putting all of the weight back on plus more. This is because they start eating again out of a hunger-and-nutrition-state-of-emergency feeling, and by the time that feeling has been satisfied, they've overdone it and put all of the weight back on and more.

(2) <u>Sports</u> - Sports is an internationally popular addiction that has a variety of appeals. I would say that the central theme of it's appeal is as a business sublimation. The conversations that I've heard or that I've been involved with over team strategies could easily rival board meetings at major companies. So then why is this a drug and not just a pastime? It's because there is no useful product or service that is directly satisfying a *real* need. It is pure sublimation and avoidance of real business and other feelings. Oh sure, it can be a stage for the working out of social issues. But that can be done without any sublimation through the news media. Sports should be a participation activity rather that a spectator activity (possibly with an occasional exhibition of the best playing at a high technical level to instruct, entertain and inspire). But feeling such as strategic concern, hope,

pride, devotion, dedication, commitment, etc. should be spent in one's own business activity resulting in a product or service that will benefit others. If there's an overflow of business feeling after a person's regular job, then they should start or get involved with a second business or some form of personal or community service.

My own personal experience with sports as a drug started growing when I found my businesses' growth faltering. Instead of finding *real* solutions and immediate actions that I could take, it was easier to pick up the sports page, a magazine or turn on the T.V. and identify with and root for someone else and be concerned about their winning. But I'm a person who is filled with a lot of business energy, and I found my habit getting bigger and bigger.

At first it was just basketball, and just some statistics. But then it grew to all of the statistics. Then I started reading the articles. Then I started buying sports magazines. Then I started subscribing to them. Then I started subscribing to the sports specialist's magazines such as Track and Field, Ring, Basketball Digest, etc. and reading them from cover to cover, experiencing senses of loss or accomplishment as reactions to the failures and successes of those who I identify with. My mornings would start with reading the sports page, seeing what sports were going to be on T.V., and then being committed to watching it all (or taping it and watching it later). I would also have to see all of the sports news programs as well as the ESPN specialist programs such as 'The NBA Today' and 'Sportslook' (Hey Roy, you're more of a sociologist than a sports fan. Give me a call and I'll come on and we'll talk about all of this). It got to the point where I couldn't just see the 8:30 ESPN sports report. I had to also see the 4:00 and 11:30 ESPN and CNN reports just in case I missed something. (This escalating-involvement pattern is typical in most drug use because a person is trying to squeeze a certain type of satisfaction out of something that doesn't contain it.) But I started noticing that this was all giving me a headache and was draining (the sure signs of unrealness). I had become a slave to the sports page, my subscriptions and T.V.. Also, my conversations were starting to be filled with sports and were feeling saccharin and draining. And I started to notice a few other things.

(I) I was watching others become successful instead of becoming successful myself.

(II) I was supporting teams and individuals, but they weren't supporting me.

(III) I was putting my fate to experience wins (and losses) in the hands of others. And I started noticing that the wins were saccharin experiences that would quickly fade, while the losses were depressing and would linger. With sports you put yourself at the *effect* of a possible losing situation. But if you were to cushion yourself against this, you wouldn't be able to totally enjoy the win. A person shouldn't give up the control of their life to other people. They should *cause* whether they are going to have a win or a loss. If there's a loss, it can be taken as a learning experience from which improvement can be made and lifelong experiences can be developed. In sports the viewer doesn't have this option. Plus there are no rewards or real contributions as there are in real life.

(IV) Identifying with sports personalities and teams gives and unreal picture of one's self-esteem (pride vs. inferiority).

(V) And last, but not least, it interferes with our relationship with God in that it violates the 1st commandment: "Thou shall not have any false gods or idols before me". Sports is very popular for drawing worship energy (as is the entertainment media). But why worship anything less than perfection, and the power that designed and created this universe (God)?

Sports is a religious sublimation also in that it usually is an analogy of the good vs. evil theme (usually with the home team being the good and the visiting team being the evil). Sylvester Stallone, when asked why "Rocky" was so successful, said that it was because it played on the emotions of the theme that is most basic to life: good vs. evil. And that this theme is prevalent throughout most of the great works of art and literature throughout history. So why not just deal with the *real* good vs. evil battle in our own lives? When you start doing this you'll find that it's filled with all of the adventure, drama, mystery, wins, strategy and challenge that you could ever want.

Given all of this, I slowly withdrew from sports and allowed all the energy that was being grounded there to manifest in it's naturally intended way. That is, I started thinking about the strategies of propelling my own businesses and life and growth, and carrying them out. It's a simple disciplinary maneuver. When you feel the urge to turn to sports come on, force yourself to turn to: pen and paper, phone, car, typewriter, computer, library, workshop, thinking creatively, kitchen, instructional books, classes, lab, garden, studio, etc.. Create something real and good for yourself and others. And allow yourself some time with it until you are into the experience of it. I've been finding these experiences to be much better than sports. Now if I were to turn to sports, I would feel like I had lazily surrendered to a defeat, and that same old saccharin experience would come on.

(3) **Television**-Well you can see how television served my sports addiction, but it can also serve as a drug for other real life energies. Soap operas are a popular replacement for romance and family involvement (and also a horrible role model for these). Also, people like to root for happy endings in movies rather than create happy endings in their own lives.

Television can also be an escape from loneliness by being an illusion of company, or an escape from boredom by being an illusion of activity and social involvement.

The extreme of being hypnotized by television was conceived in San Francisco in the late 1970's by a group called "the couch potatoes". They would stack a wall of T.V.'s (about 15) and they would sit on couches and recliner chairs in front of them all day and night. The reason that they called themselves 'couch potatoes' was because they were products of their spiritual practice, which was: transcendental vegetation (they also were into their own form of 'channeling' {with a remote box}). Yes, they transcended all of their problems by floating off into T.V. land. But, unfortunately, they also transcended the potential happy, normal, productive lives that they could have been living.

(4) **Acting**-Our own personality traits can also be drugs. We can hide behind them instead of facing,

dealing with and communicating our real feelings. We can hype ourselves into acting by suppressing our real feelings and creating other feelings and actions that we consider safer and more acceptable. Some of these acting patterns can become so habitual that we can borrow a theatre technique and do a 'character study' on the character that we've created. The character that has *become* us. But, in our drug terminology, these personality traits are drugs that have been created to have some of our real feelings swept under them. But they are not connected to our natural, inspired flow.

The point could be made: what about feelings that are spontaneous, yet are negative and detrimental? With the exception of those that come about because of mismanaged stress, unnatural activity or leaving ourselves attached to aberrant environments, although they come up spontaneously and seem to 'be in the flow', they are the results of subconsciously-imbedded, faulty, past decisions to 'act'. They were rooted in the brain as an immediate response, and were programmed and grooved in through repetitive training (that is, repeatedly making the decision to act in these ways until they became automatic). But, although they may be spontaneous, they still are acting, because they come from a man- made program in the subconscious rather than the natural flow.

Some examples of 'acting' drugs: being hyper, being bad, being subdued (self-suppressed), constantly complaining, self- induced spaciness, shyness, malicious gossip, easily losing one's temper, intellectual snobbery, worrying, flamboyance, doormatitis, defensiveness, criticalness, being 'cool', overt sexiness, jive, hype, being overapologetic, the 'class clown' (yet we've all heard about the tears of a clown), etc.. If you carefully examine these 'acting' drugs you'll see that they fall into 2 categories. (1) Personality-trait-walls that we hide our real feelings behind, and (2) compulsive behavior that we hide our real feelings behind. Go back over the list and see which ones fit into each of these two categories.

Of course, there are many more minor drugs, such as: shopping, gambling, stealing, money, popularity, seeking other people's approval, etc.. Any form of compulsive-hyperactivity or frantic-search-for-stimuli is a ' drug ', as I've defined them in this book, which is: running from our natural feelings, feedback and inclinations that we don't want to experience, or from the feeling-pressure that a backlog of problems builds up. I think the examples that I've given in this chapter are sufficient enough to give the idea though. How many more can you think of? How many are in your life? As an exercise you might want to write up some examination sheets on your drug habits. I'll give you an example of one by showing you the one I did on my sports habit.

Drug: Sports

Before:
Productivity Report
Knowing most of the statistics of most of the athletes in most of the sports, thinking about team strategies and dramas, spending many hours watching sports, the bragging rights of the teams and players that I identified with.
Results
No increase in my money in the bank, no service to people, no positive influence on the world, sublimated hostility release (and possibly causing antagonism in others), waste of time, false pride, practicing and perpetuating the experiences of antagonism, hatred, competition,etc..
Conclusion:
Sports is an unproductive waste of time, sometimes dangerous and counter-productive, and keeping me from manifesting my time, energy and concern in more positive, natural activities.
Withdrawal Plan:
Gradually turning away from spectator sport activities and turning that energy into my businesses.
After:
Writing this book, reading books (to improve my business techniques), making my dreams a reality (writing other books, making music recordings, personal growth, losing weight, improving my health, raising social consciousness, etc.), help others to grow and promote their (natural) dreams, becoming more involved with church,

working on my other businesses, etc..

Progress Report:

Day by day more withdrawn from sports, more involved with natural activity, books being completed, and feeling **much more** satisfied. This all has led to complete withdrawal from my sports addiction (and all of my television addiction for that matter). More happiness, peace, excitement and fulfillment.

As a final thought, really <u>anything</u> can be used as a drug and turned into an addiction, including religion (ala being attached to wayward, boisterous and self-centered television preachers; a guru; religious rituals and legalism; meditation; etc.); our appearance; a relationship with a person or group; sex; an ethnic identification; etc.. Some of these things can be had normally, but they become abnormal when they become an addiction. An addiction can be said to exist when <u>something outside of one's self is continually given greater priority over one's natural feelings</u>. (How to distinguish between natural and unnatural feelings will be shown in chapters 20 and 21 as well as in other parts of this book where 'the truth meter' is discussed). Once this is understood, it will become evident that it is also errant to give unnatural feelings priority over natural feelings <u>within</u> ourself.

Most of the underlying motives of the addict are normal and understandable, it's just that they miss the mark in their attempts (in terms of thoroughness, judgment and accuracy in finding the optimum attempt), or they don't go deep enough (to the root of the problem(s) that stands in the way of them fulfilling their drives). It all becomes a matter of becoming proficient in the most important of all the arts: the art of living.

What a drug addict really wants to do is: fixate on something, lose themselves, forget their problems, avoid their 'real' life, and have a higher experience. But there's only one thing that we can do this on without having any negative repercussions. And that is: 'true perfection', or perfect truth. By that I mean: surrendering to the optimum way that a human being was designed to live, so as to be in harmony with themselves and everyone and everything around them. The second part of this book will show what this design is, and the third part will show how to manifest it.

Drugs And The Arts

People who are filled with suppressed emotion are drawn to the arts (music, movies, poetry, writing, acting, dance, art, etc.) either as a participant and/or a spectator. Being like a too-tightly-blown-up balloon, they need to find or create a medium by which they can 'express' themselves. 'Express' can be meant in a positive way by meaning 'express viewpoints of higher living'. But the sense in which I mean it here is 'like an orange expresses juice' i.e. just gets it out. The greater number of artists and consumers of art these days, are engaging in the latter sense of expression. There is little moral or 'social redeeming value' in today's art. And only a small percent of it has *real* wisdom or positive insight. The people who have the too-taut-balloon problem are either looking to get in touch with their pressuring emotions and filter off their pressure through the arts, or they are trying to run from them by focusing their mind on something else (in this case the arts) so that there is no 'focus' left for these inner problems to vie for. (I would classify 'the arts' as a minor drug, but the major drugs are often found here also. They are used by the artist and the audience to help purify and uninhibit the expression.) But these are unnatural approaches to the suppressed-emotion problem. The natural response would be to allow the emotions to float to the surface, and at the natural rate in which they want to do so (like a balloon under water, suppressed emotions will continually try to float up towards the surface in an attempt to get resolved. They won't just lie dormant). Then deal with these surfaced emotions by seeking out, learning and then feeding the mind 'truth', with the 'seeking out' process being fueled by the urgency of the emotions being resolved and the power of the emotions themselves. Then retrain the mind to respond to these emotions, and the situations in our life that causes them, in the way that the 'truth' would have us naturally respond (e.g. change of environment, activity, perception, relationship or personality trait; having a specific kind of communication with someone; seeking further education; etc.). You see, when you take the 'running' approach, you have to continually run. Because the problems don't go away, and they will constantly push to be resolved. So then why not just turn around and solve them once and for all and save years of 'running' (and basically from the same problem)? But because there is a giant lack of knowing and understanding of the truth in this world, people are forced to deal with their suppressed emotions in unnatural ways (such as 'running').

Studies, of varying lengths (up to 15 years) and all over the world, of artists, that were reported in Psychology Today, stated that 38 to 43% of them were manic depressive (large mood swings caused by suppressed emotion overcoming the suppressor), and that 7% of these actually committed suicide during their study. Most of the cases of death from drug overdose are probably conscious or subconscious suicides. Probably very few are accidents. The people who commit these suicides don't feel that they can and/or want to face life so emotion-filled and solutionless. Deep down they know the dangers of the doses of the drugs they are taking but, given all of the above, they don't care about the potential consequences. And, actually, death-as-an-escape might be (consciously or subconsciously) welcome. You see, opening the can of worms of suppressed emotion is indeed moving in a higher direction, but you also run the risk of being overwhelmed by the intensity of the emotions if you believe the untrue perceptions that are attached to them. Before engaging in such an endeavor, it is well-advised to be armed with the sword and shield of 'truth', so that you don't fall prey to believing untrue perceptions, which will further intensify and create emotions that may prove difficult to deal with. And we must continually build up our armor for the rest of our lives by continually subjecting ourselves to those who have the wisdom and perceptions of the truth that we don't have.

Chapter 9
The Ramifications Of Choosing Drugs

A person starts taking drugs because they *hope* that the drugs will do something for them (e.g. control emotions, dull them to their problems, create euphoria, appease peer pressure, loosen them up, uninhibit them, give them insights, fill emptinesses, give them something to do, relax them, stop their rambling mind, etc.). They *continue* to take drugs because the drugs do accomplish some of these things for them. This is being psychologically dependent on drugs as a crutch to create these accomplishments. But taking the drug route to these accomplishments has stingers. Prices must be paid physically, mentally, emotionally, spiritually, socially and financially. Plus it's dealing with life on a lower level than need be (running, a smelly accumulation under the rug, skeletons rattling in the closet, missing out on life's highest rewards, etc.). A higher level would be to deal directly with and work on solving the problems that are getting in the way of creating these accomplishments naturally, which then, in turn, would create a euphoria. You might say " if it's so easy, then why are so many people falling to drugs? And why are so many clinics failing in their attempts to get and keep people off of drugs? ". Well, the solution is possible, but not obvious. I was a member of a number of successful (musical) bands in the 1970's and that gave me the time and financial freedom to pursue these solutions. Yet, even though I was very earnestly and actively pursuing them, and this pursuit was my number one priority in life, it still took me many years to find them (14 to be exact). Hopefully I'll be able to save many people a lot of time and trouble by putting them all in this book. Then it just becomes a matter of being able to see them and apply them to the customized path that each individual needs to travel, depending on what they already can see, and what they need to see.

A far worse situation is when psychological dependence is joined by physical dependence. Now you have mental cravings compounded by usually much stronger physical cravings which, as anyone who's ever experienced them will verify, cannot just be overlooked. This is why a person can't just 'say no to drugs'. They'll have to have something more powerful to say yes to simultaneously. I mean, why would a dependent drug user go back and suffer the same life that drove them to drugs in the first place? Drugs were, at least, some relief. Why go through withdrawal and intense pain just to return to emptiness, and/or confusion, etc.? There would have to be:

(1) a promised land at the end of the storm, and

(2) a vessel that could make it through the storm.

The second part of this book will show the promised land, and the third part will show how to get in the vessel that will get there.

But before I show the rosy alternatives to drug use, I want to show some of the potential dangers of choosing the drug route with some personal horror stories.

We've all probably heard of the deaths of sports stars because of drugs, such as Len Bias and Don Rogers; music stars such as Janis Joplin and Jimi Hendrix; and entertainment stars such as John Belushi and Judy Garland. And there are many more. All callousness aside, we're talkin' death here folks. You see, this is one place where the ' say no to drugs ' campaigns miss it. And that is, many drug addicts don't really care if they die or, at least, are barely in touch with that caring. This statement is made by the fact that they allow themselves to take potentially deadly drugs. Deadly not only from direct physical effects, e.g. comas, heart failure, choking, respiratory failure, etc., but also from things that can happen because they don't have full control of their mind and body, e.g. car accidents, drowning, falling from a balcony, falling off of a boat, etc.. They obviously would rather take the chance of dying than to live this life without drugs. Some drug users work to push this realization down into their subconscious, and some possibly are even ignorant of these dangers (with the current deluge of headlines, though, this doesn't seem too likely). But for some, death might even be seen (consciously or subconsciously) as a relief from their life struggles. That is, they know that they are flirting with it, but, in the back of their mind, they're not totally rooting against it. (But, depending on the cosmic-after-death-reality, death in this way could end up being a far more extreme tragedy than their life was).

The Possible Consequences After We Die For Having Taken The 'Sweeping It Under The Drug' Approach During Our Life

In the midst of the hyper blitz of unnaturalness that's going on in this world, I'm trying to get people to consider that they and this world were created, and that the creator didn't make this creation for no reason. And that the world is abominating this creator's perfect design, and that instead of getting caught up in this abomination until they die, people need to reflect on the possible ramifications and consequences of approaching life like this. And that they should turn and face the messages of their conscience instead of sweeping them under drugs. Because, consider this: in taking the sweep-them-under-the-drug approach to life, what's actually being swept is nature's feedback within us as to the offness of our actions. The creator didn't design this feedback for no reason. So when we take this approach, what we're doing is: telling the awesome power that designed and created this universe and us to shut up. How do you think this power feels about that? How do you think it's going to react when we die and have to face it? Actually, as an exercise, picture the day when you die, and picture you facing this power and what you might have to say for yourself.

So now what about those who, due to a fear of death or a respect for it, choose to <u>live out</u> a pain-filled life of a person who once opted for drugs as a relief, but now has *fallen* to them and their physical and financial nightmares? For the person who has sunk as far down as the slums or skid row, the cold, hard cement feels just as bad to them as it would to you and me (although they harden their feelings as much as they can to the experience, just as you and I would). Just use your imagination and picture the countless ongoing social, emotional and physical horrors they must experience. It's much more intense than what minor drug users experience. How did they get that way? I mean, no one came out of the womb that way. What untold number of shocks and horrors that they couldn't deal with knocked them down to the level that they're on? Well, people (significantly parents) are what knocked them down. But then it was probably drugs, and their side effects, that finished the job. It's ironic that what they sought relief in (drugs) eventually pushed them down further. This irony should be heavily advertised so that people who start into drugs have a realistic picture of where drugs often lead.

Here's a few shocks that I incurred along the way in my drug experimentation that drastically altered my life for the worse.

In the late 1960's I lived in San Francisco and was a musician (now if this isn't prime drug candidacy I don't know what is). There constantly was a joint being passed around. Looking back on it though, I can see that my drug use started as a yielding to social pressure. It was so much easier to just take a hit off of what was being passed around than to say no and then have to deal with the strange rejection vibe or have to try to explain why. Also, in my case, there were the business security and advancement considerations. If you didn't do ' what the guys did ' you weren't ' one of the guys ', and therefore wouldn't be considered to be able to enter into the higher business cliques because you didn't fit into their corresponding social cliques. (Stop and reflect for a moment. Are there any social pressures in your life? Are there any rules of the cliques that you're in that you're going along with, but deep down you really don't want to?) Before all of this, I was a happy, oblivious-to-tragedy, '50's-kind-of-guy. I was a newly married college student who was into music, stamp collecting, sports and my marriage. I was free, independent, not a bit self-conscious, energetic and very happy. I enjoyed nearly every waking minute of every day, constantly doing fun, exciting and adventurous things. And this went on for a number of years. But eventually my yielding to drugs, and the hippie movement, would take it's toll and turn my life from a sit-com into a horror story.

Oh sure, I could put up with the initial nausea, headaches and bouts with fear. They were actually all part of the adventure and a small price to pay for the highs. And, actually, I wasn't really afraid of anything. At least not like the painful, inescapable, bone-chilling, dooming fear that drugs would later introduce me to.

My first minor experience with it came one day at the hangout where my friends and I used to get high. I had just come from getting a wisdom tooth pulled (speaking of young, strong and oblivious, there was another time that I went to a student dentist on L.S.D.). I had been put out and given codeine afterwards to numb the pain. At my friends apartment we all sat around a large flask filled with wine and hashish, each with a tube in our mouth, inhaling the hash smoke that was bubbling throughout the wine. We would start out smoking and talking, but after a while we were so high that the talking faded into us just riding the high music of the FM airwaves. After a while I was so high that I just *automatically* continued to toke at specific intervals without even realizing it. But then eventually comes that very non-euphoric moment in drug taking when you realize that you've gone too far. With alcohol you throw up or pass out, with food you feel painfully full. But with the heavier drugs, the experience can become very unpleasant (to the point of death, or painfully just short of it). The first thought that came to my head after what seemed like hours, but was probably only about 40 minutes, was that I went too far and that I had better leave. Then after taking another 20 minutes to muster up the strength to say " I'm going to leave now, I'll see you guys later ", chills and waves of extreme fear like I had never experienced before (even during the time that I had nearly drowned when I was a young boy) ran all through my body because I was totally experiencing that ' I was my voice leaving my body '. Now I know that this is kind of a hard concept to grasp if you've never had the experience, but imagine if you did all of a sudden have this experience. You'd probably be as terrified as I was. I mean, I was just a '50's-kind-of-guy who knew nothing of mystical, spiritual, supernatural or occult type of experiences. The heaviest experience of the bizarre that I had had to this point was seeing the Boris Karloff version of "Frankenstein" (and I really ended up liking and feeling sorry for him). Well, not to make this too light, because this was the beginning of years of living in continuous pain with very little relief. It introduced into my emotional vocabulary: intense fear and paranoia, although it would take a few more years and a few more bad experiences to totally bring me into a suffering existence in the twilight zone.

Shortly afterwards I took LSD for the first time. I've often referred to this night as the best night of my life because it reshowed me God and love and, by contrast, experientially showed me how far from love I had drifted since infancy. But then when I came down and my mind became stronger and back to it's real current condition, it added a few new negative emotions to my experience. Because from the very high perspective of LSD, I saw how spiritually ugly the inclinations of my mind really were. But, not having any spiritual awareness, I didn't realize that I wasn't my mind or those inclinations. I totally identified with my mind and body. So therefore I started to dislike myself as I noticed these ugly inclinations, and it was becoming harder and harder to live with myself (which really isn't an option in this life, being that we are indelibly printed to our minds and our bodies until death). The few new negative emotions that my mind had added were self-hatred, depression and an extremely uncomfortable urgency for self change. The LSD vision might have been a real and beautiful insight, but it was a far too outgradient one for me to be able to handle at the time. It was a giant leap, whereas I needed to take more gradual steps (i.e. more gradual insights) before seeing what I saw. I saw too much of my offness at once. Much more than I could quickly change. It was so ugly that I just wanted to get it out of me. But it doesn't happen that quickly. The feeling was kind of like: if you lived in a slum all of your life and only knew of slums, then someone moves you into a penthouse and you think that it's permanent, but it turns out to be only for a short while, and then you have to move back into the slums. The feeling of living in the slums now is going to be much different than if you had never known the penthouse. This is where my sense of urgency came from. I saw the roaches and the rats and the dust and the cold and the danger and the lack of modern facilities, while simultaneously looking at the immense beauty of God and love. It was hard to handle this intense urgency that automatically went on in my stomach and head. It drove me to many psychiatrists, psychologists, analysts, etc. looking for relief, and it took me years and a lot of money to find out that they didn't possess it. I understand now what I was going through, but at the time I had no idea, and neither did anyone else that I saw. But even if I had understood it, I don't know how much good it would have done because I was involved in a physical process. Of course there were things that I could have done that would have helped, which I'll describe in the third part of this book, but there still would have been some suffering. This is why it's not good to mess around with drugs. The effects of one time usage can last for years. And I experienced worse ones than these later on (which I'll describe later in this chapter). From the effects that 'seeing too much' had on me (although they were high and good and very pleasurable visions), I now kind of understand what the Bible means when it says " no man can see the face of God and live ". The intensity and the gradient would be much too high for our minds to be able to handle.

But these experiences were very minor compared to what was to come. I had heard horror stories about people who had taken LSD and were convinced that they could fly and had jumped out of a window to their death. Or a guy on PCP who had pulled out all of his teeth with a pair of pliers. But these were hard for me to relate to as even being possible. But it's all possible for any of us. We're all just experiencers in a different set of circumstances capable of whatever those circumstances drive us to. Some of the most seemingly mighty and solid among us have fallen quite hard. Tragedy nearly always comes as a a shock and a surprise.

I finally got a taste of this one night when I took some strong LSD that was laced (unbeknownst to me at the time) with strychnine, a deadly poison that was used in very small doses to be mixed with LSD as a stimulant. Well, some amateur chemist had a poor sense of 'very small dose'. I took some with my wife and then we spent the rest of the night trying to survive. On the one hand we were extremely high and sensitive to our experience from the LSD, and on the other hand, what we were extremely high and sensitive to was the fact that we had been poisoned. At the onset we were hallucinating so bad that we could only see a blur of colors melting together but couldn't make out any shapes or forms. When it hit it's peak I had an extremely intense pain in the middle of my brain that I could in no way touch or relieve. It was at the point of where I couldn't bear it any longer, yet I had to. This lasted for several hours. I had heard horror stories about people who tried to physically rip their skulls open in response to this pain, and ended up killing themselves. Though I still tried to hang on and endure the pain, I accepted a few times that night that I was going to die. But, obviously, morning came and, with the help of some friends, my wife and I had survived. But still, even after this experience, I was pretty much emotionally and psychologically intact. I was just totally afraid of LSD and would never take it again. The most devastating blow wouldn't come until a night a few years later.

On that night, I came home and proceeded to have one of the usual growth and life-realization conversations that my wife and I always had. You see, I was still trying to grow to the point where I could live up to the state of spiritual maturity that I had seen and fallen in love with on my first LSD trip. And this was our way of growing towards that. We'd have very deep conversations in which we'd evaluate ourselves and life in terms of what was ugly and what was beautiful, and where we and it needed to grow. We enjoyed these conversations very much. They were very cathartic and always moving in a direction of a higher degree of honesty. They were extremely deep, high and relaxed. The feeling was excitement, adventure, release and realness. Well, on this particular night, we were in the kitchen and I was sitting on the counter talking, and one time when I looked up, my wife's eyes were open as wide as silver dollars and she was gasping for air in a state of panic. This immediately shot a bolt of lightning down my spine and put me also in a state of panic and shock. To make a long, ugly story short, she had taken LSD and didn't tell me, and said that she was having some sort of vision about how we were different and separate and really not one, and how all of the molecules in the room were melting together. I had only had some marijuana and I tried to talk her down. But it was no use. We were both experiencing panic and having <u>extremely painful</u> (physically and emotionally) rushes up our spine. Without going into all of the details, the beautiful oneness that we had shared in marriage for 9 years and had taken for granted because we never realized it, was shockingly gone in an instant. For days afterwards we were continually getting these intensely painful spinal rushes. I drove her to a mental clinic to get thorazene, valium or whatever it would take to bring her down. We couldn't just sit in one place and withstand the experience. The situation was urgent. Shortly thereafter we would have to separate. Because it was obvious that the effects of this LSD trip weren't going to end in just one night like they had in the other ones. We couldn't even comfortably be around each other for another 5 years without a fear of recurring rushes. And those 5 years were absolute hell. Constant, intense, emotional pain, and spending every moment trying to cope with it and survive. Seeing many psychologists, psychiatrists, etc. but not getting any answers or relief. Heavy drinking; hardly ever going out or seeing people; couldn't look anyone in the eyes, not even at the supermarket (it took years of hard work to get over this). I truly experienced what total aloneness was, with <u>nowhere</u> to turn for answers, comfort or understanding, while simultaneously suffering. I had painted myself into a corner with just myself and my wife, totally in love and one, and now she was gone. (By the way, we're back together now.)

So now, is this the kind of thing that you want to take a chance experiencing? A momentary decision to take a drug that could turn into a prison of years of intense pain? Sure, I've recovered from it all now, but the years of suffering were torturous, and I'm sure that it's left some scars. Taking drugs is like Russian Roulette, although the people who give you the drugs either won't tell you that (because they want to make the sale and/or because misery loves company), or they just don't know it. But I'm telling you this now. Be forewarned. These things could happen to you as well.

Hopefully the stories in this chapter weren't too shocking, but just shocking enough to let you know what kinds of risks a person is taking when they try or do drugs.

There are many more personal stories that I have. Like the time I spent the whole day worrying that I was going to swallow my tongue and die because I had been given some pharmaceutical cocaine and my mouth and throat were so numb that I couldn't control them or anything that was in them (this could possibly be the cause of some of the cocaine related deaths). Or collect your own horror stories of friends, newspaper accounts, and possibly even yourself. But instead of just breezing over the newspaper accounts, stop and try to picture what went on there. Then picture the same things happening to you. It will help you to bring the reality of these occurrences 'closer to home', and let you see that these are potential situations that could cause you extreme pain. This might help you to create a safer atmosphere in your life, and stay away from drugs and those who use them.

There are so many dangers that we aren't even aware of. Look at all of the deaths, family losses, personal injuries and permanent physical, mental and emotional damage caused by drunk driving alone (not to mention all of the other drugs). And all of those who died these ways aren't around to write a book or tell us in what horrifying way their death happened.

Also, in this chapter, I didn't even really talk about the inevitable, *immediate* bad ramifications of taking drugs, such as hangovers, withdrawals, declining health, declining finances, loss of relationships, etc., etc..

In an episode of "The 3 Stooges", Curly once asked " Hey Moe, I can't seem to find a job. What do you think I can be? " Moe said " maybe you can be a professional bad example ". When I first saw this I laughed because, of course, Curly would be a bad example for a person who is looking for someone to pattern their life after. But this scene from 'The 3 Stooges' kept recurring to me over the years. Actually there was a profound thought here and a key to a positive function that we could all serve in this life for each other. An illustration of this function would be: A group of people who wanted to settle in an unknown forest were standing at it's fringe. They were trying to figure out which direction to take going into it. So they sent out a few scouts in the main possible directions. One of the scouts came back saying that his direction wasn't very livable because it was just a constant slope and building on it would be difficult. Another came back saying that his direction would be great because it was near a stream and that there were fields for planting. The third came back covered with and hurting from poison oak and cuts from a bear fight.

Now for those of us who have had a few bear fights and bouts with poison oak, don't you think that it's our responsibility to come back and warn against going in the directions that have the traumas in them? But actually, the warning isn't complete unless there's also another person coming back from the stream direction telling us of a good route to go (as evidenced by the fact that the deaths of entertainment and sports stars have had little affect on drug use). Otherwise the group of people would just starve, standing at the foot of the forest. This is why I've never written about these experiences before. I had to return from the trip to the stream and be excited because I now also had something good to offer besides a tragic story that many drug users could only identify with but not be helped by. Drug users are down enough as it is. What they need is hope and solutions, not more tragedies. I've never been a big fan of tragic books, movies, songs or television shows. If it doesn't have a happy or resolved ending ('resolved' here meaning 'completely resolved' i.e. brought all the way to 'perfectly being in tune with nature'}, I think it's best that the story be left untold until the completed story can be told. I feel that any story that ends on a down note is not complete. Tragedies can be told to warn people, or inspire them to create and implement solutions. But not in the air of doom or 'no hope', as are many of the media offerings these days. Frank Capra once said that the makers of movies have a tremendous responsibility. When millions of people go into a dark room and give their attention and open their hearts, you have a great responsibility to uplift them and add to their lives in a positive way and not hurt them. These are great and caring ideas from someone who gave us some of the greatest and most uplifting movies of all time ("Mr. Deed's Goes To Town" is my favorite). I feel that this attitude should also be applied to all of the arts. That's why, in this book, I may tell about the bears and the poison oak, but I also tell about the streams and the meadows. This next section of the book will tell about the streams and the meadows (chapters 10 thru 16), and the final section will tell about how to get there (chapters 17 thru 22).

Hopefully, to some degree, you've now had the benefit of the experiences that I've had without having to go through them, or take the drugs. I hope it's given you a better understanding and a better feel for the dangers and risks of drug-taking, because there seems to be such a gap between the glamorous ways that alcohol and drugs are advertised in the media and by peers, and the realism of the many lives that they've hurt and ruined.

Chapter 10
Conclusion: Drugs Aren't
A Real Solution

So now that we've hit bottom in our conversation about drugs, let's start our climb back up and look at the rosy side of life, and describe how great it can be, and how we can make it so.

The conclusion at this point would be that drugs aren't a *real* solution, but rather a solution in the sense that saccharin is a solution for a hunger for something sweet. That is, once the semi-weird taste is overcome, the hunger seems to have been satisfied. But then it pops up again later when it realizes that it has been fooled, and this time with a saccharin stomach ache and headache to boot. The only real solution is to keep our insides clean and free of problems by dealing with them as they pop up, much the way that we deal with dust in our house when it collects on things, or the way we deal with the dirt that accumulates on our car or our body. The real problem is the lack of understanding in this world as to how to keep our insides clean. People just keep taking one wrong approach after another. And these wrong approaches are constantly being invented and reinforced in the media. It would be like taking a mud bath to get the body clean. And amid this lack of understanding, a person's inner state of uncleanness just keeps getting worse, as the backlog of unresolved problems keeps piling up. Thus the heavy inclination towards drugs that we have in our society. But drugs don't really help. They just make the pile invisible temporarily, during which time new and greater problems can fester. Therefore, what's critically needed is: the understanding of how we should and shouldn't act, in order to be in tune with our bodies and emotions in such a way that happiness is what pops up instead of negative-feeling messages (that are trying to tell us that we are acting incorrectly).

In this next section of the book I'm going to describe what the basic operating actions of a human being should be. When these actions are being acted out, the uncleanness messages are limited to nuances and backlog.

In the final section I'm going to show how an individual can discern within themselves what is natural and what is unnatural irrespective and independent of what this world or anyone in it is saying.

As for the joy-ride drugs, such as LSD, the problem here is the 'outgradient' factor that was mentioned and the fact that the roller coaster occasionally jumps the track. And when this happens it's kind of like sitting at a blackjack table hoping to win $20, but ending up losing $1000. In other words, the gamble that you make in trying to seek a *little* fun could end up in a *giant* loss. Also, the results of a car accident while drunk or high would be a giant loss.

Besides, the more we get the art of natural living down, the more we'll, be reaping positive emotional rewards.

The 'Gambling' Factor In Taking Drugs

Actually, *all* drugs had a Russian roulette factor for me. They weren't as drastic or dramatic as Russian roulette (with the exception of LSD), but still the same idea, only less intense. In other words, it was a 'gamble' every time I took a drug. With grass the gamble was: either I was going to have a good experience of being high, relaxed, happy, giddy, intensely concentrated into something creative; or a bad experience of being paranoid, introverted, self conscious, fearful, unable to physically function well, have a bad headache (especially during comedown), etc.. With alcohol it was that I'd be high, happy and extroverted for about 15 minutes (sometimes it was up to 30 minutes, and sometimes not at all). Then I'd be sluggish, wiped out, painfully drained and with a headache for a few hours. When watching sports I would either experience a saccharin elation, a depression, or a drained feeling where I didn't feel like doing anything else afterwards. Yes, drugs generally have a gambling factor and/or a price to pay. But really though, that isn't the point, because most drug users are *willing* to take the gamble, and, if they lose, pay the price, which is a statement that their lives aren't in great shape. This is stated by the fact that they would be calloused and insensitive enough to put themselves in a position where they could possibly go through some suffering. But that's what this book is all about. To increase sensitivity to 'right and wrong'. Not to just point out the ills of drug use, but to point out the more positive alternatives and how to achieve them; to inspire drug users to get up for something by showing them that there's a something worth getting up for. All people are the same in that they choose the highest options available to them. A person isn't going to give up drugs, even though drugs may cost them some money and suffering, unless a higher option is given to them.

You see, what we're dealing with is this; this is the most concise view (from a person's viewpoint) that I can give of this life: we are in bodies that give us drives and demands. When we live out these drives as specifically as their corresponding demands dictate, we experience positive feelings. When we don't, we experience negative feelings.

But our response to these negative feelings should not be to try to squelch them with drugs, but rather to see them as 'the guy from the woods who tangled with the bear and the poison ivy'. They are there to get our attention and let us know that we're going in a direction that will end up hurting us and/or others. Flowing with them is the solution, not trying to suppress them or run from them. Yes, we want to get rid of them. But instead of getting rid of them temporarily with drugs, get rid of them permanently by naturally resolving the issue that they're trying to bring to our attention.

An example of running would be: I know a woman who keeps her television on <u>very</u> loud (mostly soap operas) and then at a certain point in the day she starts drinking <u>heavily</u>. This routine is an attempt to run from her conscience. But her conscience is only trying to help her get back on the right track and stay there. But obviously she doesn't interpret it this way and prefers instead to do battle with it. But the awareness gates will not suppress what is intended to be helpful. Therefore the conscience's messages have to be continually forced away. But now this woman is starting to talk to herself. This is because her conscience is building a tolerance to the drugs that she's using to run from it.

So the whole key then is knowing how to be in touch and in tune with our drives, and allowing them to manifest as nature designed and intended them to. If it's happiness that is being sought, fighting the body does not ultimately work, but flowing with it properly does.

Drugs just put us out of touch with the *current* reality of our lives. Even when they give us positive insights and put us in higher states, this is like jumping ahead in our growth and development. We still have to go back and do the prerequisite work to get to these higher states, but now we might not feel like we have to because we've already been there. This leaves us very confused. It's like sitting in a penthouse in the middle of the air with no other floors built below us. And after we keep falling out of it, the only elevator that can get us back up there is drugs. But the elevator operator's price keeps getting higher and higher. And eventually we're going to go to the elevator and there is going to be an out-of-order sign, no matter what price we're willing to pay. And there might even be the police there to make us pay a debt that we owe.

Another way to look at it would be: if you lived on skid row all of your life and someone took you to Hawaii for a week and put you up in the best hotel, it's going to be very difficult to go back to skid row and accept it the way you did before the trip.

But we can live in that penthouse, but first we must build the floors underneath. And we can live in Hawaii, but first we must work our way there slowly and patiently.

These are some of the rewards that we can experience for doing the work of getting in touch with our drives and conscience and flowing with them in a natural way: peace, satisfaction, love, purpose, joy, happiness, excitement and comfort. And all of these would come easily and not have to be hyped into existence.

Now, these rewards are the resultant experiences of

'specific actions'. I believe that the human design is basic to all (I will support this point at the beginning of the next chapter) and in the next 5 chapters I'm going to describe what the manifested actions are in word, deed and thought that will bring the positive feelings afore-mentioned, and which will give us the emotional and physical strength that will make a decision to opt for any drug a distant impossibility (such as I've experienced for many years now).

We need to learn to operate our body, mind and emotions just as we need to learn anything else (that is, if we want them to run well). This is the art and science of living. And this science is especially important because we must live with and *experience* the results of our actions: our feelings. So this next section can be seen as a scientific guide as to which actions will produce the good feelings. Then you, in a scientific way, must prove the validity of all of this for yourself (of course, your involuntary inner feedback will have something to say about their feasibility, worthwhileness and accuracy with the truth).

Chapter 11
A Natural Life (Yields)
Not Feeling A Need For Drugs

These are stressful times for people in the world right now, due to a great lack of knowing how to correctly live. And this is especially so on one of the most basic levels: the relationship between men and women. The constant abuse of the basics of marriage, and 'the polite and respectful treatment of another human being' causes a lot of anger to be built up in the person(s) being abused. You add to this the financial abuse of working people (due to greed), the parental abuse of children (out of the parent's stress, anger, ignorance and greedy impatience), and abuse of the 'general public feeling' heaped on by the hyper greed of the media (due to their 'stress of making the sale', and their anger and greed) and you have a real mess. What outlets and alternatives do the people who are filled with this anger and stress have in this life? I mean, a pressure cooker can only stand the mounting heat for so long before it blows. Also, the stress and anger must be suppressed in order to cordially perform the social functions of this life, such as job, marriage, driving, etc.. But when an inordinate amount of stress is added to a system, something has to give somewhere. The rising state of stress and abuse in our world is being evidenced by the freeway shootings, the alarmingly high statistics of child abuse and wife beating, the murder and suicide rates, and the growing rate of drug abuse (despite public and governmental efforts to stop it).

So then what is the answer to all of this? Well, if you want to get rid of a problem, you don't deal with the weeds, you deal with the roots. You don't deal with the effects, you deal with the causes. But by the time you get to drugs, or any of the other above mentioned stress releases, you're already at the 'effect' stage. The 'causes' would be the reasons that I mentioned at the beginning of the chapter, and our lack of knowing how to deal with them. The solution to the causes is 'knowing how to live this life in such a way that stress, anger and abuse aren't the effects that are caused, but rather love, peace, happiness, satisfaction and harmony with self and others are what's caused'. In this section of the book I'll describe these 'ways of living', to a certain degree. What I don't cover, in the third section of this book I will show you where to find it. in the third section of the book. Then after the correct ways are known, it just becomes a matter of 'reprogramming our brain' (ala chapter 5), and restructuring our lives. I call these ways of life the 'natural' ways of life, because they are the ways designed by nature that nature will honor by rewarding us with good feelings, and not give us the feedback of stress, anger, depression, pain, etc. to let us know that we're doing something wrong and going against it's ways. This is not just a matter of me putting forth my opinions or philosophy on how to live, because all of these ways can be verified or not by each individual, based on the resultant feelings that go on within them. As far as judging what I'm saying as to whether or not to try it, consider where the judgments are coming from. Ignore any initial, compulsive, negative emotional reactions. They come from an enturbulated subconscious with a traumatic history. Rather, look to your intuition, sense of logic, conscience and instinct. These are far more in tune with nature and reality.

Now there are a lot of debates going around in the media as to what the correct ethics, morals and ways to live are. But I think that you have to put most of this aside and try to view life from a fresh perspective. I say this because if you judge the fruit of this world from a sensitive perspective, and see how harsh and problemated it is, and how it's just getting worse, one would have to conclude that the tree has serious problems. When I say to look at the world's *fruit*, I mean that if you take an objective view of people as they are portrayed in the media, you would have to say that people are mainly interested in the aberrant sides of money (greed), sex (lust), violence, tragedy and competition. And that they are hyper, shallow, jivy, boisterous and selfish. Love, wisdom, reverence, peace, truth, humbleness, kindness and gentleness are rare commodities, and becoming rarer. Whereas in some cultures (and previously in this culture) these attributes are respected, revered and sought. So for the individual who is seeking happiness right now, It's best to ignore most of the media as a source of wisdom. Because if what was going on in the media was wise, this world wouldn't be in such a mess (and continuing to get worse).

It would be nice to wake up one day and everything would be perfect in the world, and we could just totally relax and enjoy it. But that's not what's happening. Therefore, we each have to take a pioneering spirit and try to find out how to create goodness in spite of the offness that abounds in our world.

Now in this next section of the book, in which I describe how this life should be lived, some might say that this is just my opinion, and that there are many ways that this life can be lived, and that each individual can create their own way. But I contend that this is not true. And that this philosophy keeps many people trapped in lives that aren't working. In nature there are pre-designed right ways and there are predesigned wrong ways. And the rightness and the wrongness of the specific functioning of a human being is not open to debate. Just as the way that a specific automobile works is not open to debate. Either it's working well or it's not. And if it's not, there are specific, definable reasons. The human mechanism is just as definable and scientific in design and, also, can work well in only one way. For a car to work well, all of it's systems (mechanical, electrical, chemical, etc.) and each of the system's many component parts, must be functioning properly and working in an intricately coordinated effort. So it is also for a human being. But not only does a human being have mechanical, electrical and chemical systems, but it also has emotional, mental, spiritual and social systems.

So then how can we know which actions by us are in tune with nature's optimum-working-design for us, and which ones aren't? Well, the health of any fruit tree can be judged by the health of it's fruit. That is, if our actions produce feelings in us, and others, that are positive and unpolluted, we can generally know that they are good actions, and vice versa. So now in this next section I'm going to describe to you what I have discovered this optimum-working-design to be. Hopefully your intuition, heart, sense of logic, conscience and instinct (which are, for the most part, in tune with the optimum-working-design) will confirm these formulae for living to you. If that doesn't happen, I strongly urge you to try them out and see what fruit is produced. Life is an experiment. Your life is the test tube, and your actions are the chemicals. And if you don't want any explosions or smelly gases, it's wise to learn which chemicals will blend together peacefully and constructively. In this sense, we are all scientists conducting experiments in ways of living to see which ones will produce happiness, peace and satisfaction in us. But some of these experiments take a long time; years even. And some of our failures can cause permanent damage. And in some areas of life we only get one shot. One of the things that I'm trying to do with this book is to inspire people to not cut this experimenting process short by giving into drugs (but which I can understand them doing, due to the stresses and lack of wisdom in this world). But if they *knew* that they had a better option, they would take it. So now my job is to try to convince people, or give them hope, of the better options that I've experienced, having lived on both sides of the fence.

What most people are caught up in can best be illustrated by something that used to happen in "The Little Rascals (Our Gang Comedy)". When these kids wanted to get around without having to work for it (walking or bicycling), they used to ride around in a wagon that was being pulled by a goat. The way that they would get the goat to pull them was they would dangle a carrot at the end of a stick in front of him. This would get him to move because he would chase the carrot. And he would continue to move because he would never get the carrot because it was attached to the wagon (I think you can see how *stop*, *left*, and *right* would work).

Well, many people live their lives like this goat, with

the carrot being their feelings and emotions. The problem here is that some of these feelings and emotions come from a turbulent past, in which unnatural patterns for behavior were programmed into the subconscious mind. And now these normally unnecessary feelings are *being created* by the unnatural patterns. During these turbulent times in the past, the situation wasn't that of a "goat and a carrot", but rather "a goat being driven by a whip". Now the carrot in the present is a result of those whip-induced programs. And if we focus on the carrot hard enough, we're not going to see where we're going and what's really in front of us and we're going to have collisions.

Another way of looking at this would be: it's like we're driving around in our car with the radio tuned to a staticy station. We sort of hear the music, but the static is getting on our nerves and keeping us from enjoying the music. Then we start complaining about it. Then we put on ear plugs (drugs) to try to drown it out. But now we can't hear any music at all. And we just feel like we're at the mercy of all of this. And all that we can do is react to this dilemma. One of the points of this book is to say that we can change the channel. And for those who have only had AM (Aberrant Mind), I want to turn you on to FM (Freeing Messages.)

Actually, though, we *should* be able to live our lives on automatic pilot, just following our feelings and emotions. But because of these aberrant programs, and lack of naturally proper programs, if we do, we end up creating a lot of problems for ourselves and others. So now if we want to eliminate these problems, we have to eliminate the errant programs and put in ones that work well, i.e. ones that are in tune with nature's "optimum design for human living".

Learning To Listen Inside

Where we put our focus is critically important-"garbage in-garbage out". (Also, 'garbage in' will create a garbagy feeling inside of us.) And this is especially true in the sense of where we put it in terms of what guides our actions, and what programs our subconscious. Our past aberrant programs aren't the only carrots that cause us problems in the present. Current people, groups, media and jobs can also be carrots.

So then, where do we put our attention to get guidance for our action-decisions and our subconscious programs? Well, it all should be centered inside of us. Everything should be cleared here first. But where inside of us? I'll answer that shortly in my discussion about the *truth meter*. But first let's look at how we handle the feedback that comes from our insides when we're chasing an unnatural carrot.

If we're doing, or trying to do, something unnatural, there will be negative feedback inside of us to try to get us to stop the unnatural aspects of what it is that we're doing (or allowing to be done to us). So now we have the choice to either listen to this feedback, or to continue to chase the carrot and try to drown the feedback out. But if true, relaxed positive feelings, without negative repercussions, are what we want, then we have to learn to properly listen and respond to what's going on inside. Because the feedback here will guide us into not doing wrong things (that is, wrong from the standpoint of being in tune with ourselves and all of life), and also guide us into doing right things. But first we must know how to tune it in and amplify it's volume.

So first I want to center the focus of the reader on the feeling that would let them know whether what I'm going to say in this next section is right or wrong (or for that matter if anything is right or wrong). I call this feeling **the truth meter**. It's an involuntary, gut level response that speaks in the single-digit binary system, i.e. it's feedback only comes in two forms: thumbs up (right), or thumbs down (wrong). The way that this translates to us is that something either *'feels* right' or it *'feels* wrong'. The problem that many people have with it is that either they've been forced (and trained) to not look at it early on in their lives and therefore they've lost sensitivity to it, or they try to get rid of it's feedback because it doesn't agree with the people in their environment and therefore poses a threat. But sensitivity can be gotten back, and no environment is worth us having to give up our oneness with our truth meter for. This is a conclusion that I will try to persuade you to if you don't already have it. I think that it's a critical prerequisite to living a successful life. This truth meter should eventually become your best friend, whom no one will take precedence over, and who you'll gently but uncompromisingly protect and defend. Taking this stand may cause the winds to swirl and possibly carry you off to new places. But I'm saying that you'll end up in better places, with better people who will allow you to discover it's revelations, and be in tune with it more and more. Remember, flowers don't grow in deserts, but rather they need firm, fertile land, lest they forget what they really are. So when reading this next section, listen to and clear everything with this sense of true and not true, this sense of right and wrong. And try not to listen to the ramblings of your mind or the compulsive emotional reactions from your subconscious. But do objectively observe these rambling and compulsive thoughts and feelings, because it's these thoughts and feelings that we're trying to change. It's these thoughts and feelings that we try to manipulate with drugs. I will show some techniques and practices for tuning in and raising the volume of our truth meter in chapter 20.

So now, if you're giving the truth meter the benefit of the doubt (in this process of seeing if my methods are beneficial), the next step then would be to logically and visionally understand why it's saying what it's saying. It's good to have this understanding because we are verbal and feeling beings both in our mental functioning and our communication. After you've been practicing this for a while (or hopefully immediately) you'll come to love the feeling of being in tune, and you'll start seeing that there are only two stances that we can take with the truth meter's feedback: embracing or running. And running feels horrible.

The problem is is that too many people have gotten into the habit of listening outside of themselves. They listen to the T.V., they listen to the movies, the newspapers, their friends, society in general, their fellow workers, advertisements, etc.. But much of this is filled with greed and manipulation. There's little caring about others here, but rather mostly self-serving interests. They don't care about your emotional, spiritual and physical well-being. Their whole aim is to create (or play upon your already existing) feelings of need and insecurity. Then to hype you, jive you, wind you up, and drive you into buying their product and/or doing it their way. Also there's a definite lack of wisdom there. A lot of the blind leading the blind. But what I'm trying to do here is show you how to tap into your own personal connection with the ultimate source of wisdom. And you can never get enough wisdom. The more that you have, the more that the decisions that you make in your life will produce good fruit and lead you (and others) to better and better experiences.

So now let's get into the basic designs of this life. First let's start with the most basic relationship that you have, and that is: the relationship that you have with your self. Now that might sound a little strange, but what I mean by *you* in this sentence is: you the experiencer, the one who is experiencing this life, you in the center of your existence, the one who I am now talking to. Now when I say your *self*, I'm talking about what *you* are dealing with within your own being, which consists of: emotions, physical feelings, the truth meter, inspirations, drives, conscience, thoughts, perceptions, attitudes, etc.. And then after we have this relationship clear, we'll build our understanding of how this life should be lived from that point outward, constantly being inspected and cleared by our truth meter and sense of logic. (Some or all of these things you may already have together, but I plan to cover all bases so as to have a basis for anyone who wants to do a complete spring cleaning job on themselves). We'll talk about our home, our job, and the different relationships that we have with people in both of these places, such as mate, children, parents, bosses, etc.. We'll also talk about our relationship with the government, and other people (both individually and collectively). And once we get the true perspectives on how all of this is supposed to work, the formula becomes: the more that we transform our lives to what's right and away from what's wrong, the better our experience in life becomes. And this transforming adventure is so rewarding and satisfying that it will be easy to not allow the intrusions and setbacks that drugs cause. So now let's start talking about dealing with our *self*.

101

A major motivation that people have in this life is to try to keep peace on all fronts. To have a peace within themselves, and with everything around them. The main problem that people have in regards to this is when there are opposite requirements for peace from the inside and from the outside (or from another part of the inside). Something has to give. What I would like to encourage is that 'peace with the natural part of our insides' is given priority. Because this part of our insides is totally in tune with how this life should work and how we should fit into it (a high sensitivity to the truth meter will let us know when we're in or out of tune). We should never try to be out of tune. When we are, we are doing a disservice to ourselves, others and the entire natural order of things. If someone outside of us is expecting something different from us, the problem is with them, not with us. We have to gently and lovingly decline to play a part in their unnatural scenario. And if they can't gently and lovingly respect and handle this, then we have to gently and lovingly "split". That is, unless we want to pursue working with them on their inability to respect another person's feelings in order to preserve a relationship that has plusses in it that we want to preserve, or in a relationship that we are committed to, such as a marriage. But this can be a very tough thing to do, which is why many people take the sweeping-it-under-the-drug option. But keep in mind, in the process of trying to not offend people, we sometimes end up offending ourselves, nature and all of life.

A problem that many people get into is that they get separated from being in touch with their insides, and they primarily fixate on the outside (T.V., mate, bosses, peer group, society, etc.) and trying to keep peace with it. But of course, this not - look - at - the - inside approach is unnatural and was forced onto them in their childhood with physical, mental, emotional and verbal abuse (or threat of abuse). And now, because they're so conditioned to doing it this way, they continue to allow it to happen. This abandonment of the truth meter and our defending of it's feedback is usually brought about in an air of fear. Fear of a greater harm happening, e.g. spankings, harsh criticisms, teasings, humiliations, fights, withholding of love and acceptance, etc.. Grade schools can be very political situations and very rule - filled societies (e.g. how to dress, wear your hair, talk, act, walk, which drugs you do, which activities you participate in, which personality traits are 'in' and 'out', which radio stations and what kind of music you listen to, etc.), with consequences for not 'playing the role'. And they can be subtle or they can be violent.

A parent can manipulate their children by using emotional tactics as well as physical ones. The physical ones are more obvious, while the emotional ones are more subtle. It's the same within the neighborhood. The neighborhood can use peer pressure to manipulate the kids in it into following it's standards by making it hard for them to get what they need, which is: love, acceptance, other kids to play with initial relationships with the opposite sex, respect, politeness, etc.. So now under this pressure, a person is forced to conform to the outside in order to keep peace, but many times at a great expense to their inner peace. They lose self-esteem, they get depressed, they must live with suppressed anger, etc.. These are the prices that they pay for trying to please others at the expense of pleasing their inner feelings. These are also the feelings that set up drug use. And in the extremes: heavy drug habits, pregnancy, crime, suicide, etc.. For those who want to say and act like everything in the world is all right: do they think that these suicide victims took their lives for no reason? No, this is a statement of the extreme limit of suffering and hopelessness.

So now the quest becomes: how to keep peace with your insides, in lieu of a suppressive environment. But this may not be possible. So then what are the alternatives? Well we can't change the rules that determine if we are going to experience peace on the inside. These have been predetermined by nature. But we <u>can change the outside</u>. We can give ourself a new environment. So therefore the approach for becoming natural becomes: change our environment, if need be, and then start cleaning up *from the inside out*. As far as the change of environment goes, remember the 'trying to grow a flower in the desert' analogy earlier in the book? This is what drives people to be monks and nuns and to live in caves, meditating night and day. They are trying to block out the influence of the aberrant outer world and the affect that it's had on their mind, until they can sort it all out for themselves by focusing on their insides and see what's pure and what isn't pure. And I'm trying to save you a trip to the cave or the monastery here by pointing out to you that the truth meter is the purest thing that is happening inside of you. It will help you recognize what is pure and impure outside of you, and what you should or should not be involved with.

So in summary what I'm saying here is that a person needs to have a healthy, uncompromising approach to their environment. For instance, in the example that I just gave where I said that a person goes along with the crowd, but then because they had to go against their natural inclinations, they experienced anger, lower self-esteem and depression. What I said right after that was that these feelings set them up for drug use. But it only sets them up for drug use if they want to continue to maintain the pseudo-peace that they have with the outside, and not look at the negative feedback that they're getting on the inside. But the healthy approach would be to look at these negative feelings, (instead of running from them or trying to bury them), and do what it takes to keep them from happening (as opposed to keeping the outside happy by appeasing their unnatural demands). Because you can't change these feelings, but you can change the outside. Drugs can be a problem-laced attempt to change these feelings. Recreational drug users might say that many people take drugs just for fun, for a joy ride. But then why doesn't everyone want to take these rides? Why are some people repulsed by them? It's because the 'intensity' of these rides are relative. To a sensitive and clean person, they are too turbulent, gross and not fun. To a more calloused and problemated individual, who is not very in touch with their natural selves and/or whose life is not very in tune with their natural selves they would be a ticket out of the twilight zone and into fantasyland; or the dynamite needed to blast through a very solid wall between their manifesting self and their natural self. Now these statements are not meant to put anybody down, but just to get a person to take a realistic look at themselves, and to see if there are greater feelings available to them in life that can be more easily had. I'm saying that this is the case with all of us, and now I'm trying to inspire people to take the natural route; and then show them how to do it.

So then basically what loving ourself would be is: loving and supporting those drives and inclinations within us that are in tune with nature's optimum design (as verified by the truth meter), and taking responsibility to eliminate and reprogram inclinations that are not in tune with this design (and this would also be loving others and loving nature). It's loving the natural components of ourself, even when they sometimes emanate uncomfortable feelings. Because these feelings are just trying to let us know that something wrong and detrimental is happening, and that we're treading outside of the design. That's what they're there for. That's why they were designed in the first place. To help protect ourselves and all of humanity from our errant and selfish inclinations (although they aren't totally stopping and they do allow us some leeway, which gives us the responsibility to be selfish and impulsive, or responsible, loving beings, regardless of what has happened to us). Because if these feelings weren't uncomfortable, we probably wouldn't take any action. We would just go along with the outer flow and be bounced around by the people and the situations around us. And being that they're polluted with selfishness and unnaturalness, these aberrant traits would also become a part of our behavior and life. So now the question to ask yourself and honestly examine is: who do you love? Do you give priority to the outside or yourself? And if yourself, do you give priority to your natural side or your unnatural side? (It's o.k. to give priority to the outside, as long as it's in tune with nature's optimum design).

A clarification that I want to make here is that, I'm not trying to give the impression that we're supposed to be blissed-out all of the time, and that we should feel that something is wrong when we're not. Because sometimes we must work hard, or we must submit to a higher authority, or we must bite the bullet due to the rampant craziness that is being allowed to roam the world. But although what we end up experiencing is less than blissful, there is an even greater satisfaction deep down inside of us that we experience knowing that we're doing the 'right' thing. To me this feeling is priceless and takes precedence over all other feelings.

Something Different

Now if a person's life isn't working out to their complete satisfaction, there is one thing that they can be certain of: they'll have to try something different. But not just anything different because the hidden treasures only lie in exact locations. Many dangers of varying degrees lie in all of the other locations. One of the reasons that I'm writing this book is to turn people on to the locations of the treasures, and to warn of some of the locations of dangers that I've encountered.

Many times a person fails to recognize a treasure because they have it's location prejudged and mislabeled as having no treasure possibilities there. Here is an example of trying something different, and an illustration that a treasure could possibly be where you might not think one would be.

My friends' musical tastes were limited to '50's rock and roll in the early to mid 1960's. But one night in the late 1960's (when the hippie movement was happening where we were in San Francisco), I brought over a classical record to the house in the Haight Ashbury where we used to hang out. We were all stoned and we sat around and listened to it very quietly with intense, yet relaxed concentration. The experience of the music was intensely beautiful. I had always thought that it was, though, because I had played in school orchestras when I was younger (although my tenseness had occasionally pulled me away from being able to tune in and appreciate it). But to my friends, this experience was new. And now their ability to experience it wasn't being blocked by a false concept and paranoia about 'wimpiness', or a frantic hyperness because they were relaxed by the drug. I remember one of them commenting that if it wouldn't have been for drugs, he would never have been able to like this kind of music or see the beauty in it. The song was "The Largo from Dvorak's New World Symphony", or "Going Home" (both great titles about changing to something new and beautiful, which is also the feeling of the music). I would suggest that you get this record and listen to it. The best way would be with headphones. Close your eyes and meditate on it, and see if you don't get a swell of a feeling of beauty in your heart. Don't block it or judge it. Just go with it. Let it happen. These feelings of love and beauty are the ultimate feelings of 'home'. And these treasures are always within us, and we don't need drugs to get to them. It's just a matter of doing the natural things in life that bring them on, and then just allowing them to be. But how much inner and outer support do you have in your life that would make it easy for them to be in you? And, worse yet, how much inner and outer suppression is there trying to keep them from being in you? Examine these questions. Also, contrast the beauty of these feelings with the hyper, unconnectedness that dominates the media.

This last example was an illustration of what I mean about trying something different and getting to know new keys that unlock higher and more satisfying doors to more real and natural parts of ourselves. An unfortunate thing in this world today is that many people instinctively (and sometimes even consciously) know these keys, but are insensitive to this instinct and are just haphazardly trying the fad things. But these fads are proving to be harmful and are taking people further and further away from the optimum design. These fads are in the areas such as: relationships between men and women, how we act, sex, drugs, careers, etc.. What makes it worse is that there are so many greedy people in the media, advertising their products, that are trying to capitalize on the confused searching and weaknesses of others.

At this point I want to make some further distinctions about self and natural self. Recapping: *self* is that which is outside of 'you' (the experiencer), but is still within your body. *Natural self* is that part within your body that is:

    (1)   In tune with your whole self (body, mind, emotions, etc.)

(2) In tune with all of life (by 'in tune' in both of these cases I mean: operates in such a way as to not cause any disharmony with anything else or itself)

(3) Produces 'good fruit' (e.g. constructiveness, peace, love, happiness, etc.)

The task of every growing person is to become more and more natural, and less and less unnatural. Also, the more natural that you are, the stronger that you are. And out of the degree of your strength, you are able to help make your other relationships more natural (e.g. marriage, children, business, friendships, organizations that you belong to, your city, state, country, world and the universe in general). But only when we love, like and manifest our natural selves can we produce good fruit. It was pre-designed that way. It bothers me when I see modern pop psychology say that you must learn to love yourself (which is true), but then they say to do so by: doing something nice for yourself like going out and buying a dress. This is dealing symptomatically and superficially with an urgent problem. It's like putting make-up on a rash.

Love and Like

A husband and wife that I know were having some problems at one time in that she was misreading him, then getting emotionally upset (as a reaction to her misinterpretations), holding it in and brooding. This was her M.O. for a long time and became so frustrating to him that he developed a 'button' about it. Then one time during an argument, when one of these upsets that she had been holding in exploded, she said "...and you never bring me flowers or seldom say 'I love you' (which she had ritualistically become accustomed to)". He actually did love her and was committed to her and their marriage for life. But love is not a surface emotion. The feeling is much deeper and stronger. It is a commitment. It is a bonding. Also it is an act of the will. Whereas 'like' is an emotion, and as far as liking her goes, he *didn't have the power* to make himself like her when she was being negative and unjustly mean towards him (although many try, even to the point of putting on an act). And all that 'romance' is, is: like within a love setting. And the degree of the romance is proportional to the degree of the like.

It's the same with the relationship that we have with ourselves. We definitely should love ourselves, i.e. be committed to our welfare, growth and happiness, but we can only really like that about ourselves which is truly likable. The uncomfortable feeling of the dislike will help motivate us to change for the better. An example of this is the feeling of 'guilt'. We shouldn't always treat guilt like the plague, which is what many psychologists would like us to do. They would like us to see it as a malady that doesn't belong, and try to get us to forcefully pop ourselves into 'feeling good'. Now I like feeling good just as much as anybody else, but I like it to come easy and naturally, not through hyper, forceful means. And the way that this happens is not by dealing directly with the feeling, but by doing the proper actions that result in good feelings coming up automatically. And there are specific rules for this. And guilt is very helpful in letting us know when we're breaking those rules. The reason that most people feel guilty is because, compared to perfection (which is their natural working order), they are guilty. So the idea here is: the more that we face and solve the causes of our guilt, the better that life will feel to us (and the better that we'll feel to life).

So now in summary what I'm saying to you as far as your relationship with yourself is:

(1) Love yourself (i.e. be committed to achieving a natural, positive life).

(2) Continually work on growing in the direction of perfection.

(3) Be as honest as you can be with yourself (i.e. stay focused on the truth meter).

(4) Continually seek to know the specifics of nature's optimum design for us.

The truth meter is like an 'eye of the hurricane' within yourself. Once you find it, and become good at staying in it, you'll also be riding in an 'eye of the hurricane' through this world, and this life.

Chapter 12
What Is Love?

For the most part, life is an inner game. Even our relationship with the outer is an inner process. It starts with our ability to distinguish between healthy and unhealthy environments. Then it becomes a matter of our ability to play our role in the healthy environments and not pollute them. Then we can just relax and enjoy the exponentially increased pleasure that happens when an arithmetic number of people come together on a normal level. This is the normal way to live.

But most people who are involved with drugs have the problem of not being able to distinguish between healthy and unhealthy environments and/or not being able to be non-pollutive in the healthy environments. Therefore, what they have to start doing is, look inside and work on cleaning up what's causing their problems in discerning, relating and fulfilling their roles in a natural way. Many people aren't used to looking inside though, mainly because they were trained by heavy authorities (when they were younger) to obey them, and stay focused outside on them. A good example of mainly being focused outside would be the experience of going to a movie. Every emotional reaction and experience that you have is the result of what's going on in the movie. Then you come out of the theatre feeling high (that is if you went to the right kind of movie), because you haven't even noticed your problems or typical mental patter for an hour and a half or so. But, of course, then reality slowly creeps up on you as you see the real environment and your conscious and subconscious patter start evaluating what you see and what it is that they think you're supposed to be doing. And this patter consists of thoughts, attitudes, perceptions, ideologies, emotional stances, etc.. And any problems or untruths programmed in there will just tend to keep recycling themselves, with us having to experience the resultant emotions that are created as normal reactions to them as if they were true (an important thing to note here is that these mental things will present themselves open for change *each time* that they come up. So therefore, it's very important that we acquire the right data to reprogram them with).

So what I'm asking you to do is to develop a strong focus inside. Now that you're in there, what now? Do you take the traditional psychoanalytical approach and start dissecting your problems and try to discover their roots? My feelings and experiences about the effectiveness of this approach can be best expressed by what Woody Allen said in "Sleeper" when he had just found out that he had been awoken 200 years after he had been put to sleep. He said "you mean it's really 200 years later? Wow, if I would have been seeing my analyst all of this time, I would have almost been cured by now".

So then, if psychoanalysis is not it, what is? I think that it can best be described by this analogy: If you're in a dark room you don't just stand there, curse the darkness and try to figure out how you got there. You first find the light switch, and then you turn on the light. Because where there is light, there is no darkness. And once the light is on, you won't care about the darkness or hardly remember that it even existed. You'll just be getting on with enjoying the light, and trying to perpetuate it's presence in your heart and life.

You see, the whole point here is that no one is really concerned about the darkness. They only concern themselves with it because they think (or hope) that this will get them to the light. But if a direct route to the light were shown to them, they'd take it. So now I'm going to proceed to show you where the light switch is.

If you were trying to learn to play tennis well, do you think that it would if someone just told you what you were doing wrong? No, they'd also have to tell you how to do it right. So now, in this game of life, I want to describe how to do it right. First of all, what is the light that will illuminate a dark room? It is wisdom, it is the support of nature, and it is a feeling. And this feeling is the feeling that occurs when we are acting correctly. So one way of approaching it is to learn how to act correctly (which I'll cover in the next chapters), and the other way to approach it is to learn how to be in this feeling, and to be able to distinguish when you're in it and when you're not. I'm going to call this feeling: "love". Although there have been many different feelings that have been labeled 'love', the one that I'm talking about here is the optimum basic feeling of life. I'll make it clearer by defining it's characteristics. Then you can tell if you're in love or out of love by if you're fulfilling or violating any of it's characteristics. We can take this outside-in approach to love because the feeling of love is, by nature, 'just there'. It doesn't have to be acquired, just not gotten in the way of. The negative of it's characteristics are the warning signs that's it's being left or has already been left. And when we see them, we can adjust by subtracting the negative behavior (inner and/or outer) that is causing this change. The 'inside-out' approach would be to: add the correct behavior which would cause love to happen. This approach will be dealt with in the next chapters.

The Bible does the best job of describing this love that I'm talking about, so I'm just going to simply quote a few verses from the Bible to describe it.

(1 Corinthians 13:4-8) "Love is patient, love is kind, and is not jealous. Love does not brag, and is not arrogant. Love does not act unbecomingly. It does not seek it's own, is not provoked, does not take into account a wrong suffered, does not rejoice in unrighteousness, but rejoices with the truth. Love bears all things, hopes all things, endures all things. Love never fails".

(Galatians 5:19-21) Love is not "immorality, impurity, sensuality, idolatry, sorcery, enmities, strife, jealousy, outbursts of anger, disputes, dissensions, factions, envying, drunkenness, carousing,"

(Galatians 5:22,23) Love is "joy, peace, patience, kindness, goodness, faithfulness, gentleness, self-control,"

(Galatians 5:26) "Let us not become boastful, challenging one another, envying one another".

(Excerpts from Matthew 5:3-16) "Love mourns, is gentle, hungers and thirsts for righteousness, is merciful, is pure in heart, is peacemaking, is persecuted for the sake of righteousness, is the salt of the earth, is the light of the world, produces good works."

What I'm talking about here is a surrender to perfect truth, which has a certain underlying feeling to it (but which can trigger a range of emotions). But just like you can't transmit to another person what the feeling is like to taste tropical fruit, you can't transmit what the feeling of love is. But you can describe some of the components of the feeling e.g. sweet, smooth, slightly tart, very delicious, etc.. Similarly here, I've been describing how a person's behavior manifests when the feeling of love is in them, which is also a peripheral way of communicating what the feeling is. The best way that I can describe what the feeling is is also by saying what some of the components are. The feeling is a deep, quiet, still, solid, knowing-that-what-you're-doing-is-right satisfaction. And when love sees love outside of itself, the emotions can range from peaceful to happy. When it sees a lack of love, the emotions can range from solemn and purposeful to grief. Now understand, this feeling is the basic feeling of life and should be in us all of the time. If it isn't, then we can immediately know that we're doing something wrong in word, deed, thought or in our subconscious.

On the following two pages is a checklist of what love is and isn't and can be used as a moment to moment indicator as to whether or not we are (or someone else is) in love. If you know the feeling that I'm talking about, can you think of any other attributes that can be added to this list? If so, write them in. Also, mentally survey your personality and relationships in this life and see how much of them are in love, and how much of them aren't. This checklist will give you an idea of the work that you need to do on yourself, and will also show you what is and isn't working properly in your life.

LOVE

IS	ISN'T
Patient	Envying
Kind	Boasting
Rejoices in truth	Rude
Protectful	Quick-tempered
Trusting	Grudges
Hopeful	Provoked
Perservering	Impatient
Positive	Offensive
Growing	Unkind
Bearing	Cynical
Grieved by evil	Giving-up
Responsible	Negative
Giving	Arrogant
Knowing God	Uptight
A gift from God	Put downs
Seeing everyone as equal	Demanding
Hungering for truth	Nagging
Self-control	Irritable
Perfect order	Resentful
Sensitive	Money-loving
Compassionate	Conceited
Considerate	Complaining
Empathetic	Pessimistic
Harmonious	Selfish
Relaxed	Whining
Contributing	Conniving
Constructive	Boisterous
Creative	Argumentative
Submissive	Greedy
Uplifting	Taking advantage
Helpful	Destructive
Forgiving	Frantic
Caring	Critical of goodness
Humble	Delighting in evil
Modest	Stubborn
Gentle	Insensitive
Cooperative	Spiteful
Self-sacrificing	Revengeful

I've given 3 exercises to do here, and I highly suggest that at some point you do them. Because you've been taking a lot *in* in reading this book. But it's also good to get something *out*. Because in order to program these concepts into your subconscious and make them second-nature, you'll have to go over them a few times and think about them. These exercises are a good way to do that.

Here's a good story that exemplifies what love is and what love isn't.

In the late 1800's in England, two men, who were nearly totally paralyzed, shared a hospital room together. After being there for a while they became good friends and shared their pasts, philosophies, feelings and secrets. But the time in the hospital often became boring and tended to make them focus on their physical pain. So to cheer the other the man up, the man by the window would often describe to him what he saw outside of the window in great detail. He described the pond and the ducks and how happy the children were when they fed them. And the flowers and trees and people having different types of interactions. But after a while, the man who was hearing these stories started to notice that his feelings of love for the other man were turning to envy and anger because he wanted to be by the window. One night the man by the window started choking, and the other man, who was the only one who could reach the nurse's buzzer, just lay there and did nothing. The choking man ended up dying, and in the morning they came and took his body away. The other man waited until things had calmed down and it was politically appropriate, and sheepishly asked if he could be transferred to the bed by the window. His request was granted and he was moved to the bed. As soon as the attendants left, he struggled in his paralyzed state to sit up and look out of the window. All that he saw was a blank wall.

How often are you the man by the window, and how often are you the other man?

Selfishness is the opposite of love. And all people have this ugly seed in their basic nature. But that doesn't mean that we have to water it. Also, all of this isn't to demean why people sometimes become callous and self-centered in this life. For one, it can appear to be a dog-eat-dog world, and many may have become this way because they've been burned and hurt by others. But now we must leave all of that behind and take on a new life. And that new life is what I'm now trying to describe.

Chapter 13
Love Inside First

So now that we know the characteristics of love, the formula for creating it is a simple one. And that is: approach all of our actions <u>within the guidelines of these characteristics</u>, and the feeling will be there. See these characteristics as absolute rules for living. Clear everything that you say, think or do with these characteristics, and if there's an 'isn't' present, try to squelch it and act out an 'is'. Of course, you're not going to be able to act out an is unless you philosophically agree with it. So give each of the is's some thought, but in the meantime, as a part of your experiment of testing this approach, just try to act out some of the is's and see what fruit is produced. If good fruit is produced, it will give you power and momentum to continue this process. Because, if you look very carefully, you'll see that we have many decisions that must be made every second. This is where we primarily need to insert our reflection on whether the characteristics of love are being violated or fulfilled. My testimony is: knowing these attributes of love has been extremely liberating for me. That is, liberating me from many pain and trouble-causing mistakes that I would have otherwise made. Also, liberating me to act and think much more properly than I would have, and as a result, I'm able to enjoy the good feelings that naturally come from doing so. Also they've gotten me out of many jams that my old nature would get me into. Maybe a bad feeling would start, but I didn't have to let it continue, because an alarm would go off and my stomach would start squirming, and having studied the attributes of love, and having realized that this alarm and this squirming were in tune with those attributes, I've developed a quicker respect for them. Now my approach is to try to turn the off switch, instead of speeding by them. And I've always got one eye on them and the truth meter. Kind of like someone

117

who's got a radiator problem. They're always drivin' with one eye on the temperature light. Actually though, the better you get at it, it'll be like trading in the temperature dummy light, which doesn't go on until you're in real trouble, for a temperature gauge, which shows you when it's just starting to get hot and if there's a problem brewing. This is great, because it's much easier to deal with an engine when it's slightly hot and you have some warning, than to try to take off a radiator cap when it's boiling. You have to wait for it to cool off, and hope that no damage was done in the meantime.

Another thing to consider is: how are we going to spend money if there is no money in the bank to spend? That's why it's critical that we learn how to create (actually *allow*) the feeling of love inside first. And then from that fullness, we'll be able to approach life with something to offer, instead of walking around like mini black holes, draining everyone's love and energy with our psychodramas, unnaturalness and selfishness. (The 'mini black hole' analogy doesn't include natural, sincere needs.)

So, in our inside-out approach to analyzing life, we need to start looking at all of our specific relationships and see if love is being violated anywhere, or if an aspect of love is missing.

The first relationship that we encounter is our relationship with our 'self'.

Are we 'patient' and 'gentle' with ourselves? Or are we overly 'critical', 'impatient', 'demanding', 'compulsive', etc.? Go up and down the list of is's and isn't's in the last chapter and examine if your relationship with yourself is one of love, or if there are some things that need to be eliminated or added on.

This relationship with self is probably the most crucial because, if it's right, there will be an abundance of inner love and strength to fuel all of the interactions that we have in life in a positive, natural way. If it's not right, the resultant air of stress and negative feelings will make the rest of life's interactions that much more of a burden.

The World's Influence

This world does not make it easy to be real, natural and normal. Most people are deluged by a constant bombardment from a negative and greed-oriented media, that is filled with actors and actresses that are being paid to serve as role-models for unnatural living. (This may not be obvious, because we've become very callous to it in order to just be somewhat at peace and not constantly be upset. But if you look at history, societies didn't collapse overnight. It took a succession of moral break-downs. And each of these moral breakdowns took years for the public to give in to. And not without a lot of public outcry against them coming on. Can you see how things today can actually get much worse. I mean, what's happening today in pornography, sexual and romantic morals, etc. would have been horrifying to the societies of decades ago. But this evil was allowed to gradually creep up on us. And do you think that it's going to stop here? No. It won't. Not in a permissive society. So stop now and imagine what's going to come next? Actually, don't.) Realness, naturalness and normality should be obvious and all-pervasive in this life. Instead, it's like hidden treasure that is hard to find. Like I've said, I had to spend 14 years actively searching until I found it. The unfortunate thing about the over-abundance of role-models for unnaturalness, and the severe lack of role-models for naturalness is that: <u>Until realness and natural-ness are found and merged with inside of oneself, the outside cannot be related to in a real way, and merely becomes a stage and players for us to attempt to live out our inner psychodramas and confusions.</u> In the sense of relating to others, as long as the environment is safe, the urgent priority has the inner taking precedence over the outer. Because to *truly* experience someone, you must first be *truly* seeing them. If we're looking at people through filters of: misperceptions, labelings, prejudg-ments, generalized attitudes, how-they-can-be-manipula-ted-to-fulfill-an-unresolved-psychodrama-need, character-relating-scripts-that-are-emotionally-aberrant, etc., then we're not really *being there* with them. We're stuck in our own inner world. And an inner world that is in this condition will require a lot of education and transforma-tion before it will release us. And in essence this means: reconnecting to our natural functioning. Then the clean-er, more weightless and more filterless that we become, the more that we'll be able to truly be with others, experience *them*, and be a part of the oneness.

This is looking at the problem of unnaturalness from a person's viewpoint. Now let's look at the *social* manifestation of the problem from an over-viewpoint of all people. Let's start by looking at just two people, within the setting of a marriage. On the one hand you might have a person whose real self is internally buried to some degree (which means that some of their behavior is stoic and/or hyper). And they might be reading the other through some unrealness (filters and psychodramas, as previously described). Now here's what really makes this a mess: the other might only be showing a degree of realness themselves and also misunderstanding and misinterpreting the other due to their filters and psychodramas. Another problem here is when a person's automatic responses come from the 'not shown to self' area, and they either misinterpret their own responses or they don't even see or recognize them. So now what you have as the result of all of this complication is: unrealness relating with unrealness as if it were realness (two different and separate realnesses, I might add).

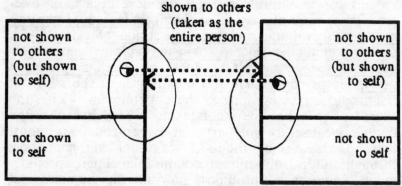

Now if you expand this to include all people, you can see the enormity of the mess (yet how unapparent it is), and how realness can stay so hidden. Only operating and finely tuned truth meters can see through all of this and sort it out.

A mahatma once stated that one of his main goals was "for his heart to be like an open book, and that anyone could easily see all that was in it at any time".

We need to examine: are we that open and honest about what goes on inside of us? Then we need to examine: what have we got to hide, and why?

By nature, we shouldn't have to hide anything. Protectively covering up dark secrets only allows them to fester and destroy ourselves and others. If we expose them in an environment of wisdom, we stand the chance of getting the counseling that we need to rid ourselves of them.

So the only solution to our (and the world's) problems is that we get in touch with 'realness' (that is, what's *really*, and completely, going on), and then do the work of transforming that which is unnatural into being natural. And this isn't going to happen by hoping that the world (others) will change first. We must first do this work inside of ourselves, and then out of our clarity and fullness, we can do work in the world. Because the more real and natural we become, the more free we become, because our consciousness isn't being tied up by our problems, and subconscious attention isn't being tied up to hold the inner problems in check. And with this new freedom, wisdom and vision, we'll be able to see into all three sections of people (from the last diagram), even where they can't see themselves. We'll have the freedom and untied-up problem-solving energy to not only work on our own remaining offnesses, but those outside of us as well. There's an old song that nicely expresses what our approach should be: "Let there be peace in the world, and let it begin with me".

The Art (And Science) Of Living

The reason that I write books is because I see many people that are very unskilled in the art (and science) of living, and who do many short-sighted things that end up hurting themselves and others. But this is the opposite of what we're trying to achieve, which is: peace, pleasure and satisfaction.

We are all on a ride, each in a human body, on the planet earth in a universe. We do things with our bodies, and there are resultant experiences. We all desire these experiences to be: peace, pleasure and satisfaction. So then why do we spend so much unnecessary time in: pain, frustration and enturbulation? It's because we make and carry out the wrong decisions for what our actions, thoughts, words and life settings should be. First recognize that we do not have free reign. We are riding in a very intricately designed existence. So the smart thing then is to learn the rules of this design, and do what brings peace, pleasure and satisfaction (without infringing on anyone else's natural peace, pleasure and satisfaction), and avoid what brings us pain, frustration and enturbulation.

Our Relationship With Our Mind

If we are concerned about the quality of our feelings, then it's important to know the role that our mind plays in producing feelings in us. First, it's important to note that our emotions *react* to what our conscious and subconscious minds say to us *whether what they are saying is true or not*. This is an important operation of the mind-emotion mechanism to recognize. To prove this to yourself, close your eyes and fantasize a tropical situation....or a scary situation....or a romantic situation....or an angering situation. Didn't your emotions react as if they were true? But they weren't true. This is why the work of transforming negative emotions is done in reprogramming the mind and not by focusing on the emotions themselves.

This leads us to another very important realization. Many people live aberrant lives because they are slaves to faulty programming from traumatic pasts. They're still trying to get the parent's love that they never got, but that they needed to feel good about themselves and their natural feelings (I mean, if the parents don't see the beauty in their children, or enjoy them, It's a slim chance that the child will see their own beauty or enjoy themselves, or even believe that they're beautiful and enjoyable to others even though they really are. To me, this is physical abuse, because the emotions that this causes can be just as painful inside as outer physical abuse causes. Hurt is hurt). So they dwell on trying to resolve what their parents did give them in place of the love, and try to transform it into love. For instance, a parent may not have been capable of real, gentle love, and wanted to mold their child into what they (as opposed to nature) wanted them to be. So they used the

122

tactics of badgering and belittling to break down the child's self-confidence, and didn't satisfy their children's need for their love and acceptance, therefore putting them in a weakened position whereby they'll do anything to please the parent (which is the moldable state that the parent wants the child to be in so that the child will accept their unnatural demands). But now when this child grows up and their feelings want to restore them to being natural, they have a dilemma on their hands. They have all of these tape recordings from their parents in their subconscious as to why they shouldn't allow their natural selves to manifest, and why they should live out the unnatural demands of the parents. And these recordings, when gone against, trigger insecurity and fear. So now the grown up child is still being badgered (but now it's by their subconscious and the emotions that they trigger) and they are yielding to this badgering's demands on their behavior and attitudes. But on the other hand, their adult natural self wants to rebel against this and return things to normal. You see, the natural course of events in their childhood should have been: parent's love; (leads to) allowing the child to be their natural selves and lovingly guiding them away from unnaturalness; (leads to) the child being able to flow with their naturalness; (leads to) the child feeling good about themselves. And all of this love and feeling good is nature's stamp of approval on the proceedings. Now if it didn't happen this way, many times you'll find adults stuck on the first step, still trying to get the parent's love. And usually this manifests as them trying to prove their parent's criticism's and belittlings wrong. For example, if a parent harshly told their child that they were ugly, their child might spend their whole life extremely concerned about trying to improve their physical appearance to the point that the parent's criticism wouldn't be valid and they wouldn't feel the harshness any more and they could finally love themselves. But this approach will never work. And that's because you can't transform tape recordings from the past. No matter what you do, they still say the same thing. You'll never get love or acceptance from them. You'll just become a person who is obsessed with their looks, but deep down feels bad and is never satisfied. At best, you'll feel a semi-satisfaction, but you've unnecessarily been a slave to a tape recording and wasted a lot of time, money, suffering and concern. And the hurt still remains that your parent would ever do this to you in the first place. But you're so caught up in this that you can't even see that this is why you feel bad.

And this tape recording will never be satisfied, because it can't be changed. It's just an inanimate tape recording.

The only solution here is to get a "parent transplant" to a parent who is *really* capable of loving you. Many people attempt "parent transplanting". But if they pick the wrong parent and they once again open their heart, and are once again disappointed, they might turn to drugs and, if it's a return visit, try to stay there (because they've now lost hope). They won't be freed until they find the one (and only) natural parent that we all share in common. And that parent is the power behind nature itself. And this parent really is the ultimate authority over all of us (as will be proved in chapter 20). It is the power that created us. Call it nature or God, but by the end of this book, this relationship will be very clear. And it really is capable of giving us that parent's love and guidance that we need to give us the strength to stop the aberrant, critical recordings in our mind that make our emotions make us feel bad. Then we can move on to the next steps in the 4 step process that I just mentioned that (lead to) us feeling good about ourselves.

The whole point here is that: it's no use debating in a situation where we have no chance of winning the debate. It will just upset us, and possibly destroy us by inundating us with bad feelings, such as depression, self-hatred, etc.. Many people who *seemed* to have it all, ended up killing themselves (Marilyn Monroe et al). Could the things stated here have been the reason? We just need to find the new, natural parent's love and acceptance, and live within *it's* guidelines, to maintain that love and acceptance. But it will be different this time because it's guidelines are perfectly in tune with our natural self, and there will be no inner conflict between what it wants and what our body wants. Then out of the strength that we'll have from this new parent relationship, and from the momentum of flowing with our natural inclinations, we'll get better and better at being able to stop the tape recordings if they try to start up, and know that it's just a waste of time to even think about debating with them. Our only communication with them is to let them know that they are not needed because they are untrue, cruel, and merely the aberrant ramblings from the selfish interests of people in our past, and that they don't bring about any good for us or anyone else in this life.

And there could possibly be many such tape recordings in a person (that they are trying to use drugs to silence). But the Bible tells us to "guard our mind" against listening to such evil. That means actually standing guard and simply not letting them in. Then eventually, if you're living a natural lifestyle, and have a restored relationship with your natural parent, nature itself (which all earthly parents should allow anyway, and never get in the way of), and have stood guard over your mind, these recordings will get the message and stop playing on their own. This has been my experience. They don't care. They are just inanimate recordings. But we have to tell them to stop playing. And we can only do this if the function that they're filling is being filled somewhere else (i.e. parenting). Otherwise we will be approaching them as needy, instead of with strength.

Now the questions to ask yourself are: did you or do you now have parental support to be natural? Did you or do you now have parental pressures to be unnatural? Are there any critical tape recordings that you are trying to resolve, or trying to sweep under a drug? Or are you listening to these tape recordings, regarding them as true, and living under their thumb? Well, you don't have to live like this. But you need to get rid of these aberrant recordings and fill the parental void that they are currently, inadequately filling. You need to make perfection the only thing that you look up to, instead of unnaturalness and unnatural people. By the time that you've completed this book, you will have the tools to bring this whole mess to normalcy.

Chapter 14

Our Relationships With Others

So now, given that the basic (and optimum) feeling of life is love, and given that it can be made to exist by either an inside-out approach (in which we cause it to happen by restricting our insides to only approach the outside within the guidelines of the 'is' characteristics of chapter 12), our next concern is the outside-in approach. This is where the love is made to happen inside because we're doing the actions outside that are in tune with nature's-optimum-design for each specific situation that we're in. Once again, the specific actions that will produce love are not open for debate or design. Just as which direction that a car will go when it's steering wheel is turned to the left is always the same, we have a similar situation with these specific - actions - that - produce - love rules. With these next chapters I hope to save people a lot of painfully failed, trial-and-error, experiments in them trying to find out these rules. But I realize that a person must be convinced before they'll change their acting patterns. I hope to convince them.

So now the important thing is to know the basic rules for our actions that will produce positiveness in each of our specific relationships in life. In essence this means: knowing the specific ways that all of the aspects of life were designed to function optimumly. Reflect for a moment on my previous 'systems-of-a-car-working-in-sync' analogy. This reminds me of my time in college as an engineering student. There we were shown how the physical universe and all of it's components worked and interacted. Every relationship was exact and could be described measurably in precise mathematical formulae. Likewise, if we want to live life successfully, we need to be *life* engineers, and we need to understand life as precisely mechanical engineers understand the physical universe.

So now our next order of relationships, as we move outward, are the ones that we have with our immediate family in our home. In the Bible, many rules for living are given and expounded on. But Jesus made it a point to say that the most important of these was "to love thy neighbor as thyself". The Bible also says that it is good to do good deeds and exercise spiritual gifts, but without love, we (in spite of the good deeds and spiritual gifts) are nothing. It also says that "he who is least among you, this one is great". And that "blessed are the meek and the gentle". These really are essential components of the optimum design. Do you think that the world is moving further away from or closer to living out and supporting these truths? Are you as an individual moving further away or closer to these truths?

It is essential to love and respect your real self and your natural feelings. But it is just as essential that you do this for others. Many marriages and families have problems because a person (or persons) see that they should be respected and treated nicely, but they don't see their responsibility to respect and treat others nicely. This is selfish. "It is better to give than receive". Implicit in this statement is that our gains should never happen because we plotted another's loss. We can use our work to *create* new gains, just as others should. Life should be a situation in which everyone wins, based on mutual contributions.

If you look at it, you'll see that life is a continual political situation of every individual trying to get what they want. But only in the natural-perfect-order can everyone actually get what they want (because in the perfect-natural-order, people only want what they naturally need. All other wants are the result of sublimation and selfishness). In it, every want is perfectly designed and coordinated so that there aren't any clashes. The problem is that many people don't know what they really want. They'll get an *idea* (which is mental and unconnected) of what they think it is that they want, and then they'll pursue trying to make it a reality. But if this idea is wrongly reading their feelings of need and is unnatural, they end up 'taking' from life to fulfill it. But then there has to be a loss somewhere to keep the balance of 'give and take' in life. The way that we can know if we're in the natural-perfect-order or not, is if we are within the characteristics of love or not, and if our actions are in tune with the perfect, natural designs.

Let's focus on the key relationships that we have to others and see how this love would manifest. That is, in keeping with the automobile-systems-in-sync analogy: if love is the gasoline, let's look at the specific system designs that allow the car to work.

Like the ants, we are social beings. That is, when we're functioning at our best we are each specializing in a few of the jobs of living and relying on others to do the rest. And all the while with everyone maintaining an integrity and responsibility for doing a good job. In this sense, a person in Miami has a relationship with a person in Wisconsin, although they may never see each other. So now specifically, the key relationships that we have are:

(1) Our mate
(2) Our children
(3) Our family
(4) Our friends
(5) Our business relationships
(6) People in general (individually)
(7) People in general (collectively)
(8) The universe (life itself)

As for our relationship to the universe, I'll deal with that in chapters 20 & 21.

Our Mate
Be very careful in selecting a mate. They can either make you extremely happy and at peace, or could possibly keep you so emotionally enturbulated that you will be driven to drugs and/or barely able to function in life. The oneness that you enter into together has this much power (that is, assuming that you fully enter into it in your heart).

Entering into a relationship with a mate is kind of like flypaper: very easy to put together, and very difficult to pull apart. And every time that one of the mates does something unnatural that tests the glue of the relationship, it has a very painful and dramatic effect on the feelings of the other. Much more so than the other relationships in life. This is because the security of the lifelong commitment in a marriage is very important. The reason being that 'very helpless and dependent beings' (children) are relying on that relationship for their security, survival and development. One of the major problems that we have today is that the government usurps the role of the father by freely doling out welfare payments. It allows the mother to not have to take responsibility for making the relationship with her mate work. And then puts the burden for her and her children's livelihood on the public (who probably doesn't even know the great extent to which this is going on). Or there's the unfair situation of the absent father having to support a household run by a selfish woman who probably has problems just like him, but the legal system unfairly favors the woman and he's not allowed in the home to give the children an alternative to the mother's problems influencing them. Really the laws in this country concerning man-woman relationships are very out of tune with nature's-optimum-design. Given the flypaper analogy, and being that the emotions are very intense in male-female relationships, negative emotions from these relationships that are going wrong is a source of the fuel for much of the world's problems. By nature, divorce should be illegal (with a very few drastic exceptions). Setting up a marriage should take a longer time, and possibly there should be some legal qualifying steps as the process is unfolding to test the abilities and sincerity of the two parties to create a real, natural marriage. I equate the process of preparation for a marriage and having children to 'nest building'. It takes time and that much care. And all done within the feelings of 'romance' and 'falling in love'. Many marriages are thrown together with very shaky nests (which is why they fall apart). The woman should be testing the man to see if he can be a good provider, a loving mate, a good spiritual leader and a loving father. The man should be testing the woman to see if she can be a loving mother, a good homemaker and a loving mate. But because of the lack of wisdom, patience and low moral standards in the world, people put the blinders on, and haphazardly throw relationships together, driven by their sexual impulse and shaded by their deep-down fear and lack of hope about a marriage working (based on the ones that they've seen in the world). But the nuclear family is the most blessed of all of nature's relationships. Yet, judging by what people are experiencing, there aren't many who are receiving these blessings.

A marriage can be made up of grossly selfish, insensitive people, in which the conflicts will be dynamic and obvious. But it can also be made up of moderately incapable people. In which case, the experience was best described by (I think it was) Socrates: "The person who finds a good mate becomes happy. The person who finds a bad one becomes a philosopher".

So you want to find a mate who is fully willing and capable of carrying out the key functions in a marriage. Any offness in any one of them could prove to be emotionally unbearable and lead to arguments, fights, walls, being drained, sadness, uptightness, loss of good emotions, insecurity, upsetting the children, etc..

So then, what are the requirements for a successful marriage?

(1) A commitment for life.

(2) A desire for it to work nicely.

(3) An ability to surrender and submit.

(4) A realization that a perfect person doesn't exist.

(5) A developed ability to recognize and bridal any word, deed, emotional impulse or thought that would prove to be harmful.

(6) Taking responsibility to keep it working.

(7) Each partner taking responsibility for making sure that their own happiness and security are maintained within the marriage.

(8) The ability to communicate and hear communication with mutual respect and caring for each other's feelings, without attacking or judging, and with objectivity and love.

(9) Seeing yourselves as being one and being on the same side, and being in and surrendering to this oneness. (The opposite of this would be seeing yourself as being separate, or pitting yourself against the other.)

(10) Never taking the attitude: I'm dissatisfied. I'm leaving (or thinking about leaving); but rather: something's bothering me. Let's talk about it nicely and work on it.

And all of the above has to be done by both parties. And when this is all done, the basic feelings of love, happiness, peace and security will be there (not to mention the absence of negative feelings trying to warn that something is wrong). These are nature's rewards for doing the above work. Aren't they worth it? A proper relationship can be so fulfilling and energizing. The problems come in when one or both partners won't fulfill their end of the bargain, or they take the energy being flowed to them and spend it on unnatural, selfish pleasures, or to try to resolve past traumas in a sublimated way.

Another thing that aggravates problemated male-female relationships is the number of sex idols in the media (and we do get a constant barrage) with their deteriorated morals and out-of-tuneness with nature's optimum design. But of course this is only the tip of the iceberg of the very deteriorated problem that we have in this world with modesty. People should only 'doll' themselves up when they are especially, and out-of-the-ordinarily, trying to get someone's attention to their physical selves. And this should only have to happen during courtship and within a marriage. Nowadays many people are in a constant 'dolled-up' state. And just to do things like pass on the news or weather information, or sell a product, or even just walk down the street. But, sadly, it's even gone beyond the 'attracting interest' phase. It's directly into a 'creating - sexual - feelings - in - others' (which really only belongs in the domain of the bedroom of a married couple). People are showing more and more of their bodies in the media and in public. But this is just pulling the world further and further away from nature's-optimum-design and making it very difficult for people to achieve a natural male-female relationship within it.

In the following chapters, the other relationships that I mentioned will either be covered directly, or peripherally by dealing with their various aspects.

Business

In business there is a fine line as to how much we should get as compensation for our labors and contributions. If we're getting too much, 'guilt' is nature's message that this is the case. If we're getting too little, 'the feeling of being ripped off' is nature's message. So the optimum in our business relationships is to ride the fine line where neither feeling is coming up. And the feelings of the fine line are peace, happiness and satisfaction. Negotiate ahead of time and let the feeling of the 'fine line' be your guide. Then once you reach an agreement where you and all parties concerned *feel* satisfied, and this agreement isn't tainted by greed or unnatural sacrifice, you can put all of this aside, pour yourself into your work with a clean mind, and 'whistle while you work'.

Our Basic Attitude

If we ever have problems being with people, it's usually because we are not willing to 'love' them (ala chapter 12) and 'give'. Also, our basic groove should be 'gentle and meek', and we should let 'exuberance, excitement, leadership and happiness' come and go very naturally and in a relaxed way, rather than hype ourselves up to these states and try to make them our basic groove. And if we love and give and are humble, this doesn't mean that we are being doormats, because nature will give to us on the level where the greatest treasures of this life lie: our feelings. Besides, we will be promoting the perfect-natural-design by allowing others to experience the good fruit of it's ways, and we will be making it easier for others to fall into this groove. We will be illuminating the natural, relaxed way, rather than the hyper worldly way. And if we are being taken advantage of, we make and attempt to clean up the situation, or break relations.

Politeness

Politeness is a dying art. It's the lubrication that makes the social machine run smoothly. And It's merely a one-way concern that can be practiced by all. And this practice is to continually ask yourself the question: "am I making life easier for others?", or "am I selfishly hogging the social spaces that I'm in?"

Politeness can be practiced in conversation, driving, walking, business, just being around others, etc.. Any harshness is not politeness. Politeness and humbleness go hand in hand. Take a day and carefully observe yourself and others in terms of politeness. How developed are you in this important social skill? How developed do you see others as being? How much do you add to or subtract from the positiveness of the general social feeling? Are there any people in your life that you've stopped respecting, and who you find it easier to be rude and impolite towards? A key thing to note: does your politeness towards someone come and go as your need for them comes and goes? It also has a relationship with stress. If we're stressed out, it will be even more stressful to be pleasant and polite. But something is going to eventually have to give somewhere (unfortunately, the home is where this somewhere usually is). The idea here being that there is never a reason for being in a continued state of stress. Make a low level of stress the constant, and your life priorities and actions the variable, rather than the other way around. Your life, and what you contribute to others lives, should be filled with quality rather than quantity.

It Is Better To Give Than Receive

Sometimes we're filled with energy and we don't know what to do with it. So we end up trying out one of the world's latest fads for attaining pleasure. But many times the pleasure isn't as intense as the neon was bright, and we just end up causing ourselves frustration and being drained. But here's an approach that might make many self-centered hedonists cringe, but that they should take notice of. When you're filled with energy, instead of trying to figure out which hyper entertainment venue you're going to pour it into to try to seek satisfaction, think of someone or some charitable organization that might need your energy and help. Then phone them and make arrangements to give them some of your time and energy. It could (and probably would) turn out to be one of the most satisfying things that you've ever done. Plus, if you can just look beyond yourself and your insatiable search for gratification for a while {if you're lucky enough to be in that position}, you'll see that there are many people out there who can't help themselves and really need some help. And there are many organizations set up to help them, who are dependent on getting volunteer help from people like you. And then do this on a regular basis. You will probably receive great spiritual and emotional blessings for doing so (and isn't that what you're seeking in everything else anyway?). I'm saying that when the media promotes selfish, pleasure-seeking lifestyles, it misses the mark as to where we should put our energies and where the greatest satisfaction's lie. Nature has a way of looking out for it's needy ones by using very pleasurable emotional rewards to motivate the stronger ones to help them. But first you have to try this to see if it's true. Plus you'll feel much better about yourself and what you're doing with your time and your life. "It is better to give than receive" is only a paradox until you understand and experience the fact that the giver also receives.

Chapter 15
Raising Children

My infant son Timmy usually just lays around, and either his mother, myself or his brother is with him and showering him with love, gentleness and happiness. He then smiles, laughs, coos and makes joyful noises, which in turn fills our hearts with joy and happiness. And all of these rewards are positive signs from nature that right things are happening. (In the cases of colic and teething, the scenario is different but the love is the same and we just hold him, walk him, comfort him and offer him a finger or a teething ring to teethe on when he wants one). He is a very happy, content, mellow baby and rarely cries (only for physical reasons). This is because he knows that we care and that someone will come to see what he needs and make sure that he's taken care of. He knows that we're all very attentive of him and that he doesn't need to cry, so he just makes little noises and bobs his head up and down to let us know that he's awake and to get our attention (we sometimes call him 'Bob' for this reason). He's such a delicate little creature who is totally dependent on us for his happiness and survival. To think that any baby would get any less than what Timmy's getting breaks my heart. And especially so because I know that many babies are getting much, much worse. (They are such beautiful and innocent little creatures that it's hard to imagine how anyone could mistreat them.) And then many of these babies grow up and futilely try to fill voids from their harsh and unfulfilling childhoods through their present relationships and circumstances, and in doing so, end up also having unfulfilling adult relationships. And as each generation imprints and builds on the past generation's aberrations, it just gets worse and worse. Whatever happened to the sweet, happy, loving woman who was a caring homemaker, wife and mother? Or the peaceful, happy, loving man who was a good provider and a revered spiritual leader who kindly, gently and lovingly guided his family and gave them wisdom? And the happy family setting where everyone could be secure in being able to rely on the fact that mom and dad and the brothers and the sisters and gramma and grandpa and the aunts and the uncles and all of the cousins would be together until they died? Well, unfortunately, times have changed. <u>But nature hasn't</u>. Nature hasn't given up it's beautiful plan of a loving, secure, stable family. The 1950's sitcom "Father Knows Best" is a good example of the type of family unit that I'm talking about. And nature's plan is still carried in each one of our hearts, no matter how much pain, anger, ignorance, hopelessness, cynicism and selfishness that it's buried under. And we will *feel* that something is missing until we fulfill it's plan. But people often times try to erase this *feel*ing-void with drugs (major and/or minor). Part of the problem is that people might not even know that their natural inclinations are okay, and might suppress them by yielding to the pressure of the popular negative labels of: corny, mushy, wimpy, syrupy, etc.. Most of the role models in the media aren't happy, peaceful and natural, but rather, they are hyper, selfish and dramatic.

But all of this starts in infancy and childhood. Our responsibility as parents is to not put into our children something that they must struggle in their teenage and adult life to get rid of, or leave something out that they must painfully search in their teenage and adult life to find. But our approach doesn't have to be mental and contrived. It's as simple as showering them with love (in a natural way), and being sensitive to them as human beings who have as much value as we do, whose feelings are deserving of as much respect as an adult's, who are very sensitive, and are formed by how we are towards them.

A general rule for raising children would be: be totally involved with them, but in a relaxed loving way. (I mean, it would be nice of you to give a person a ride to another city if they needed one. But if you're just going to badger them all the way, it would be nicer if you just let them find some other way to get there.) Enjoy the experience. Just be your natural self and respond. There's no need to get heavy, mental, contrived, or try to force anything on them. There's no need to fix something if it isn't broken. They'll have all of the appropriate questions at the appropriate times for you to inject your guidance. But if you're a selfish tyrant they'll probably never ask and have to get that guidance somewhere else.

I can hear some voices saying now though "Oh sure, your baby is mellow and happy now. But what you're doing is *spoiling* him and you're going to have problems later in that you'll have a spoiled, bratty, selfish child". My answer to that is that we've raised our other child, Tonio, in the same way and he's now almost 7. And quite the contrary is true. He's still mellow, nice, happy, polite, unproblemated, respectful and loving. I think that with-holding love and forcing on unnatural rules is what *spoils* a child. The suppressed responses of anger, pain and frustration (to speak out) against past and recurring unnaturalness is what sets up rebellion, brattiness and hyperness. I'm not saying that total permissiveness is the way to go though. This would be denying and suppressing our natural, parental instincts to guide. But what I am saying is that this guidance can be passed along very gently and lovingly. And if it's done this way from the beginning, the child will be very receptive and smooth about accepting it because they will sense that it's being done out of a caring for them. Some say "spare the rod and spoil the child". But this phrase has Biblical roots, and the rod being talked about is not a "hitting" rod, but rather a "guiding" rod that shepherds used to <u>gently</u> guide their sheep back into the flock. I imagine occassionally the shepherd would have to get a little heavier than 'gentle', but if this is done right and with love from the beginning I don't think that it ever needs to get harsh. It's all a matter of love, patience and having the right wisdom. This grossly misused phrase should read "spare your loving guidance and spoil your child". And it must be remembered that children each have their own truth meter and there will be an occasional "why", both to qualify your guidance, and for their own mental under-standing as to why things are the way they are, and how these things fit into the greater scheme of things. The reason why many parents get hostile and emphatic at these "why" questions is because they don't have the true answers. But it's their responsibility as parents to either find these answers, or nicely and honestly say that they don't know. But if you do give them the true answers and satisfy their truth meter and sense of logic, they will be satisfied and stop asking why. And these answers will serve them for life and be the foundation of their wisdom and the patterns of their behavior.

The reason why I put the 'raising children' chapter *after* the 'love' chapter is because you can't spend what you don't have. That is, in order to give your children real love, you must first be filled with it yourself, and know how to maintain your filled state (a most important art indeed). And when it comes to children, we need a plentiful supply of love and patience. If we're stressed out or experiencing negativity or emptiness, we aren't in a good position to be able to deal with their energy and needs.

Imprinting Is A Two Way Relationship

We have a heavy responsibility as parents knowing that our children, in many instances, are going to 'imprint' us, i.e. blanketly *imitate* us, no questions asked. One of the questions that we need to ask ourselves, as caring parents, is: are we being aware of how we're being around our children, and in what ways are they imitating any bad qualities that we might have? Of course, if we're enturbulated, stressed out, caved in or self-concerned, we're not going to have the energy for this concern. Once again, the prerequisite concern is that we are filled with love first. And this will result from us cleaning up our insides and being natural. But we shouldn't use 'stress' or 'an empty heart' as an excuse. We have a heavy responsibility towards our tender-hearted children.

The Home Sets The Patterns For Relating Outside Of The Home

If children are suppressed, ignored, spanked, emotionally abused, not cared for, etc., they are not being allowed to practice normal social skills in communicating, relating, formulating and expressing ideas, etc.. They'll then go to school, and other social venues, where they'll be given a greater degree of freedom, and then start to try to express themselves in a normal way. But it will probably be shaded with self-suppression, hyperness, or anger as a result of their emotional traumas at home. And because they have these inadequacies, not having been given the chance to develop the normal skills at home, some kids at school will sense this, make fun of them, and try to dominate them. Or they will be avoided because of their harshness. (The harsh ones will especially have a hard time later in romance, which is a very delicate, nice and sensitive way of relating.)

An example of this is: one of my sons was just beginning school (the first grade) and he was feeling out to see who would be his friends. When his mother went to pick him up, she always noticed that there was this one kid who was by himself all of the time and sometimes crying. So we told our son that it would be a good idea to try to make friends with him because it was obvious that he needed a friend. Also because this other kid that our son had been trying to make friends with was playing snob games with him and trying to get him to do bad things. So our son approached the lonely child and tried to make friends. But when they would play games, this child would eventually lose his temper, get short with my son and yell at him. But you see, he was just recycling the abuse and weird games that that he learned in his home and that he was victimized by there. The sad tragedy here is that, because of the bad actions of his parents, he loses in both places. This is probably why he was crying. He was suffering at home, and then he couldn't shake the bad effects that his home was having on his relationships outside of his home.

A common outcome out of all of this, over time, is that the harsh kids further cave in the suppressed kids with their abuse. Then the 'cave-ins' find other 'cave-ins' to associate with and do 'cave-in' activities to deal with the pain and the anger that they've been storing up through all of this, e.g. drugs, crime, etc.. And the 'angry ones' find other 'angry ones', and the 'snobs' find other 'snobs', and the 'jivers' find other 'jivers', etc..

The solution to all of this is: they need to be in a

positive environment and be supported to acquire the natural communication and living skills that are needed to successfully live this life. Then they'll attain some success, feel good about themselves, and go after other positive successes inspired by their rewards. Thus the snowball will now be rolling in a positive direction, instead of the negative one that's been going on. But the hardest part is to get that snowball rolling. Because when you've been living in the desert all of your life, it's hard to not to believe that an oasis is not just a mirage. But this just means that some inner work needs to be done simultaneously. When people are having problems with their lives, many times it's not the life that's the problem but rather how they're seeing it. But if the snowball's direction isn't reversed, teenage and adulthood could turn out to be one long tragedy of aberrant living being tainted by the unresolved childhood traumas. It's a parents responsibility to try to see that their children are spared this and aren't set up for it.

Teens Who Aren't Loved By Their Parents.....And Drugs

The desire to not lose a parent's love (even for an instant) is a great motivator in a child's life. The child wants to relax and be able to count on the fact that they can consistently bask in the warmth of their parent's love and support, and then relax and go about the business of being a child, i.e. grow, play, develop, learn, formulate viewpoints, etc.. Similar to a flower growing in the sun's warmth. But what if the parent isn't capable of experiencing consistent (or any) love for the child because of their own trauma or self-centeredness? Then what's to keep the child to continue being good? What have they to risk by doing bad? Certainly nothing from the parent relationship (they might even see it as a gain because they will get their attention). And maybe when all of these angry and pained children (angry and pained for not getting their natural due, i.e. loving parents) get together, the peer pressure might be to do bad (which is a logical turn of events, given their pain and anger). And even if they don't want to go along with the bad, they might do it anyway for fear of losing their only source of love, i.e. their peers. But there's another character in this messy plot. Nature. It is within them in the form of their conscience and natural inclinations (which it designed). They can fight to turn it off by using drugs, hyper behavior, and intense focuses (entertainment), but this approach won't yield true peace, happiness and satisfaction. It's just a desperate, impulsive reaction to their circumstances. The way to achieve true peace, happiness and satisfaction, i.e. with body, mind, self, nature, and others, is to: (1) make and keep peace with nature within ourself, and (2) make our peers be people who also have achieved this, and are committed to achieving this more and more. In other words, have peer pressure and support to do what's going to be good for us and others. In my experience, this is the only way to make and keep peace. Especially in the beginning stages. Falling in with the 'wrong' crowd will only make our efforts very difficult and may cause us to fail, because we'll get tired of having to explain and defend ourselves.

Runaway Teens
Did you ever stop to look at how tremendous the risk is that teens take when they runaway these days? They end up in horrors many times (drugs, prostitution, violence, disease, pregnancy, abortion, living in the slums, crime, etc.). What this says though is how bad things must have been at home. Many times kids run away just to get *away* from what's tormenting them. But then once they get out there and find out how scary and dangerous it is, they phone a runaway hotline and many times end up back at their home. But the goal and the job of their transformation was never accomplished. It is one of my hope's that this book will inspire some well-meaning people, who really care about teens in trouble, to help them complete the job of their transformation by showing them what they're really trying to transform to, and by giving them a setting to do it in. You can't just run away *from* a problem. You have to have something to run *to*. You have to fill the void with something that works. You have to run from the problemated life to a new, natural life. And this new lifestyle has to really be able to bring peace, happiness and satisfaction. Otherwise, what was accomplished (other than stabbing out in hope, only to

find a different version of unnaturalness, with it's own variety of problems and rewards)? But this book hopefully will make it clear as to what works and what doesn't. Then maybe after peace, happiness and satisfaction are created in a person's life, they can go back and help those who were incapable of being normal, natural and kind for them. But first and foremost, the focus must be strongly on them achieving transformation themselves, no matter what it takes. This transformation can be helped and supported by <u>capable</u> halfway houses, churches, foster homes, private schools, runaway homes, and friends. By capable I mean: knowledgable of the truth of what a normal lifestyle is, and how to help a person make the transition to one.

As far as their parents and the possibility of staying home goes, there are one of two possibilities.

(1) They and their parents can break down and mutually repent of the lifestyle that caused the problems in the first place, and vow to change it in an air of love and enthusiasm.

or

(2) If they just get criticism and scorn as a response to this suggestion, they will need to take the responsibility to clear up their lives for themselves, and find a support group to help them do it. Their parents should be this support group and are failing if they aren't. But nevertheless, putting all of these unfortunate circumstances aside, there's still a job to do.

Chapter 16
Submitting To The Oneness

Modern thought has tended to see 'submission' as a dirty word. I'm sure this is so because of all of the leaders who have abused the power and responsibility of their positions. Positions in which people submitted to them, e.g. corrupt politicians, greedy employers, physically and emotionally abusive parents, drinking and philandering mates, bossy bosses, self-glorifying religious leaders, egomaniac teachers, etc..

But nevertheless, this abuse doesn't change the natural order of things. And <u>for peace to be restored, the natural order must be restored.</u> And part of the organization of that natural order is that there has to be leaders, and people submitting to the leader's authority and directions. Of course, in turn, the leaders have to have a high degree of integrity, technical knowledge, wisdom, accountability, and love for those who are submitting to them. And the people submitting to them have to be able to trust that these are in tune with the natural-perfect-order. Actually the leaders are submitting to their duty and responsibility to those who are submitting to them. In perfection, this would be enough. But in real life, where selfishness and incompetence are real factors, there has to be those whose job it is to understand what good performance is for a leader, and to keep an eye on how they are doing.

Modern thought is also trying to say that humans are evolving and getting better at living. Take a look around. Do you think this is true? If were living at least as far back as the 1950's you know that this isn't true. Maybe we've progressed technologically since then, but the quality of family, social and personal life has regressed. The disease of selfish hedonism, coupled with a lack of legal and social restraints, has been gradually destroying all that is good. The Bible says that only a good tree can bear good fruit. And where there is bad fruit, the tree also must be bad, and in need of examination. You see, in many ways, man is not evolving, but rather, like the music group Devo said, we are caught up in de-evolution. That's why the fifties are so popular now in movies, fashion and music. People are yearning for a cleaner, more natural life. And the fifties definitely were a higher, happier time. But in the process of trying to work out some of it's problems, 'we've thrown the baby out with the bath water'.

And media advertisers have always been right there to greedily take advantage of the situation. I mean, the supposedly modern women in the cigarette ads aren't examples of a higher lifestyle for women. They're just selfish, drug-pushing models.

I'm sure that some women are meant to work and have careers. But not have a job and a family at the same time. Being a housewife and a mother is a career and a full time job, if properly done. To be good at it you must be learned, well-read, trained, wise and up-to-date in nutrition, medicine, cooking, cleaning, raising children, home economics, sewing, etc., etc.. These each can be careers in themselves. Plus (and I don't think the media makes this clear or impresses this), being the mother of an infant is a full-time job. And this is full-time in the strongest sense of the word: 24 hours a day. The baby, at first, doesn't sleep for more than 4 hours (and that's if you're lucky) and, if you are loving, sensitive and caring, you must continually and instantaneously be on call to feed, burp, change diapers, give attention to, or just hold. The husband can help, but only to a degree because he has a full-time job and must get his sleep (whereas the wife can take naps with the baby during the day to catch up on her's). This is nature's job specialization in the family. And as far as the mother working outside of the home and leaving the baby to be bottle fed, if this were o.k., then nature goofed when it made breasts. And they weren't put there as an option. Human milk is designed for humans, and cow's milk was designed for cows. The protein/fat ratio is higher in human milk than in cow's milk, just as the protein/fat ratio is higher in a healthy human body than in a cow's body. So now how can a responsible media allow the illusion to be put across that a woman can have a career and children too? Now, these ads, that I used to just overlook, are looking very gross. Actually, in the social sense, I feel that they're criminal. The only possible excuse would be ignorance. But these facts have been around for a long time, and I guess we need to keep bringing them to light.

So now, what is the attitude, commitment and feeling of nature's optimum working order? The attitude is submission, the commitment is willful devotion and love, and the feeling is a combination of peace, happiness, satisfaction, 'whistle while you work', and determination to endure and get through the hardships. And nature honors our submission with feelings of happiness, relaxedness, feeling full and satisfied, and just feeling good about ourselves and what we're doing. Nature punishes the abuser with guilt, unhappiness, emptiness, boredom, and low self-esteem.

Of course, we are in a world filled with abuse, and if we decide that we just want to be a good person, we will suffer some of it, and not seek revenge. But by being very selective in choosing our environment, people and activities, we can prevent a lot of this.

So now, what is the natural order of submission?

A woman submits to her duty to her family, and to her husband as the leader of the family (but of course feeling totally free and unafraid to give her honest feedback and creative input). Men and women are equal, sharing partners in their family walking side by side. But in every situation there must be a leader who is making it their responsibility that everything is working well and moving forward. A woman in a family has enough other things to worry about that are her responsibilities without having to lock horns and try to take charge in matters of family policy. It's not that she can't steer the actions of her family, but she must first convince her husband, whose responsibility is the family actions, that her ways are right. Just as he must convince her in her areas of responsibility. Kind of like an employees relationship with their employer. This is not an ego trip, but rather a matter of things working well, and feeling good while they are working. Submission is a two-way (hopefully) feeling of love, dedication and responsibility. To get a good idea of what this feeling is, mentally survey the relationships in your life. There are probably some in which you are submitting, and some in which you are being submitted to. The best way to get the feeling of submission is to think back to your childhood. Did you look up to your parents, teachers, other adult relatives, older kids, peer group leaders, the policeman, the fireman, media idols, the government, etc.. Who are you looking up to now? Your boss, your mate, the television, the local baseball team? And when we submit to someone, we should be experiencing a feeling of admiration (at their ability to do a good job in the areas in which we're submitting to them). Now let's look at it from the other position. Is there anyone submitting to you? Do you have children, are you an employer, or a leader of any social groups? If so, do you take your responsibilities and duties to others seriously or lightly? Do you take advantage of your position? Are you stubborn about pushing your ways, or are you friendly and open for suggestion? These are all important sides of submission. Unfortunately much evil is done in submissive relationships. But that doesn't change the fact that it's still the best working order. And when it's happening right, it's extremely liberating and a wonderful feeling.

A man loves his family, is devoted and committed to them, and submits to his duty of being provider, protector and spiritual leader. He must also submit to his employer.

The children submit to their parents, and everyone submits to the government and people in general by being polite, nice and fulfilling their social obligations.

Now before anyone freaks out and feels like I've asked them to give away all of their rights and power, let me make one important clarifying point. Submission doesn't mean total submission or completely losing yourself to a tyrant. It means submitting to the proper working order. The Bible says to "submit to the government". But it also says to "render unto Caesar what is Caesar's, but render unto God what is God's". This means, follow the natural order of submission, but when you see a problem that is going against the natural order of how things should go, don't submit to it. But, if it's safe, respectfully contribute your insight. Because, in the natural pecking order of submission, a person's relationship with nature and naturalness has the highest priority. That means over self, mate, family, friends, government, job, others, etc.. But this is no act of disobedience or threat to anyone. It would only be a threat to greed and ignorance. But a big problem today is that many people try to solve these problems by getting out of the relationship. And government and our mobile, permissive society, in which distance and anonymity are easily had, have made this easy to do. In some extreme cases this is wise. But in most cases: If you're having a difference of opinion with the captain, you don't jump off the boat. You accept your part of the responsibility of the relationship and make every effort to make it operate correctly. Even if that means being patient and taking time and effort to make things work right. What might help you get through these situations is for you to think of a time in your life where someone had to be patient with you.

So now there is just one key submission that I haven't elaborated on (and this is *the* key submission). If it's understood that the natural ways are the right ways in which everything works together perfectly, then we need to know these ways and submit to them. Just look at it logically for a second and realize that there has to have been a designer of those ways. There has to have been a central intelligence (and I don't mean the CIA). Actually it's more like the engineering department of this existence. An intelligence that is completely on our side, collectively speaking ('individually speaking' would be the selfish approach that has caused the chaos that we're in).

But how do you know the source of this relationship? And how do you know that you know the source of this relationship? This is biggest problem that people have in this life. Because if you know the source of this life, then you know the natural perfect order. And if you know the natural perfect order and obey it, your life works smoothly. And if you know that this perfect order was created by the same power and intelligence that created this universe, it makes it so much easier to follow and submit to it. Being that this relationship and understanding is so important, I want to give a much fuller treatment to it. It's critically important that a person knows and understands this relationship personally, intimately and on all levels (mental, emotional, logical, physical, visional {right lobe}, experiential, etc.). I will give this fuller treatment in chapters 20 and 21.

Oneness And The Media

There is a very pleasurable feeling of 'oneness' in all of the relationships in our life where there is mutual submission. When the actions within the oneness are in tune with nature's-optimum-design and in tune with nature's calling for the individuals involved, the feeling is very satisfying. Much more than twice as good as when there is only one person involved. The saying about a marriage: 1 plus 1 equals 11, is very true. And this exponential increase in feeling good when two or more people are coexisting cooperatively, honestly, submitting, and in tune with nature is true for all relationships. But what if some of the actions are not in tune? Well then the feeling of the oneness becomes a negative one, and misery is exponentially shared.

So now, where can the state of the oneness of large groups of people and entire societies be gauged? In past cultures it was the market place, the town gate, the town hall, the churches, the playhouses, the forums, etc.. Today it's 'the media', which consists of television, newspapers, magazines, books, radio, recordings and movies. But the problem here is that these venues have financial as well as social considerations, and are very much influenced by their financiers and sponsors. So therefore, many times, the public's (and most certainly, nature's) interests are sacrificed for the sponsor's interests. And what is their rock-bottom interest? To sell their product, not to promote peace and social welfare. So, therefore, the prevailing feeling in the media is the same as that of a hyper, unconnected salesman. And the Bible says that "money is the root of all sorts of evil".

The most unfortunate thing in all of this is that there is a snowball effect in the negative direction. Because new generations are heavily influenced by the media, and are somewhat formed in it's hyper, shallow, over-dramatic, unnatural image. And the older generations may take for granted the fact that they were more exposed to realness, and not see that the new generations aren't.

And there are so many attempts to sell more-intense-than-natural comedy, drama and lifestyles. One of the purposes of a laugh-track is to try to hard-sell a joke or comical situation that the producer's are afraid won't get enough of a laugh on their own merit. And because of the pressure of how hard it is to make a living in the media (if you average out over all the numbers that are trying), only the very driven succeed (and most of the time it's not 'driven for the sake of the public'). But because of this, they're in such a frantic state that the stories that they push are frantic. A heavy flavor of their drive is: the constant fear of rejection and job loss. From the producer's standpoint it's the constant panic for new, fresh material and also the loss of their job. These same paranoia's are shared by the writers, actors, network employees, crews, sponsors, etc.. And all of this manifests as this frantic desperation to titillate and lure the interest of viewers who make up the ratings. And when you're this hyper and unconnected from nature, nearly anything goes. That's why the media is constantly testing the limits of morality and human behavior. Because when you're unconnected and unsatisfied, anything goes. Everything becomes a desperate attempt to reach out for satisfaction. In the desperate, hyper air of unconnectedness, most fantasies have equal value. It's like being in outer space with no gravity. There is no frame of reference. No moral guidelines (except the pursuit of money and how to fool whoever stands in between). Their consciences are seared.

One of the selling angles of the media and it's advertisers is that they try to make people think that they're 'missing out' on something. Then people ruin their marriages, finances and health chasing these rainbows. All the while not noticing that they've been sold a bill of goods by actors, and that many of the people who have achieved the pots of gold at the end of these rainbows many times end up in suicide, disease, divorce, etc.. And this must only be the tip of the iceberg. Many illusions are allowed to be perpetuated by the aforementioned 'wooden box' condition of this world. The pain outweighs the pleasures by far in most of these rainbow chases, and what pleasures there are, can't hold a candle to the natural pleasures that are possible in this life. Save your money, health and marriage and learn to listen to your truth meter. This will lead you to the places where real treasures are.

It's funny how each time I opened a door to a new treasure, I experienced surprise. Surprised because I never thought of these things when I was looking for treasures. They were always there but I had overlooked them or misjudged them. And many times this was due to another's opinion that I had taken from the media or from peers (who might have gotten their's from the media). And the thread that ties all of these treasures together is 'love'. As opposed to the threads of hyperness and greed that seem to permeate much of today's fads, activities and media offerings. Each treasure is just love showing another side of itself. There used to be much more love in the fifties. For us to return to this, the media's basic feeling would have to return to love. And people's morals and actions would have to become more in tune with the perfect-natural-order.

So now we must be aware of the many relationships out there that can offer us a 'oneness'. Because many of them are 'polluted with unnaturalness'. We don't want to submit to these. We first want to submit to naturalness, and then find relationships and groups that are also devoted to this. And, if need be, start our own groups. But eventually we do have to accept the realization that people are imperfect beings and sometimes are incapable of love and naturalness. But if you attach yourself to someone or a group that is too incapable, the constant enturbulation and depravity can be enough to drive you to seek relief in drugs. So an important part of the solution then is for us to associate with others who are devoted to naturalness, and who are already capable of a good degree of naturalness. Then we can keep to a minimum the amount of compromise that we might end up making with nature. This would include associations on a job. Of course, there is an attribute for people in social situations that can greatly smooth over unnatural behavior and it's effects. And that is humbleness, which could manifest in apologies. If we are like this and others that we are around are like this, then the love and the oneness can continually be restored when they are broken by unnatural behavior. And the situations can be mutually beneficial as opportunities for growth (i.e. being given the opportunities to point out to each other our weaknesses for succumbing to unnatural behavior patterns). But definitely try to avoid arrogant, defensive, argumentative people. It's rarely productive and not worth the enturbulation and potential trouble.

Chapter 17
Making A Commitment
To Improve Your Life

One of the things that I'm trying to do in this book is: give people such a vision of the truth, and the great possibilities that are within it, that it will inspire and *empower* them to make a commitment to elevate the quality of their lives to the levels of these greater possibilities. Because they will need a lot of energy, determination and single-mindedness to do the investigation and transformation work necessary for them to be able to 'add onto' and 'eliminate from' what they need to in their lives. And the speed, joy and effectiveness of this work will be determined by the accuracy of their visions, which will in turn inspire them emotionally and give *strength* to this emotion. So, basically, I'm talking about the natural (not forced) strength of their commitment. By *natural* I mean the pool of strength that is just naturally there for them to freely and easily spend on the right things. By *forced* I mean that people are sometimes committed to things that are unnatural, in which case they have to force themselves to do the things that it requires, or use artificial sources of strength, such as drugs or aberrant peer and social groups, to help them carry out their requirements. But it is much better, and feels much better, to commit yourself to what is true, natural, and meant for your life at this particular time. Because nature will give the strength necessary to carry these things out. Whereas it will be draining, a waste of time, and possibly harmful to pursue mentally inspired pursuits (as opposed to naturally inspired pursuits). It's much more pleasurable to go through life with a natural and easy peace, strength and satisfaction, than to hyperly and frantically struggle to pull off unnatural desires.

So then, what are the elements that increase or

decrease this strength of commitment? This strength is regulated in the subconscious based on (1) what the conscious has seen and how it's evaluated these visions, and (2) the degree of how in tune these evaluations are with the ultimate truth. If a person went to Hawaii and experienced the beaches, water and weather, and these had a positive affect on their feeling, they would have a strong commitment to return and would be willing to make the necessary time and money sacrifices, because they would already know the value that they would get for their sacrifice. But if a person has never been there, they would have to rely on how convincing someone who's been there was in their description. And then still they might have the thought, "well, it was great for them, but I might not have the same experience". Or another might say "I really don't like the sun and can't swim, so I won't have a good experience like the other one had". Now I don't think that these last two analogies pertain to this book because I feel we are all basically the same, so therefore personal preferences don't enter into the picture (although I do believe that we each have a personal timing and gradient in our growth and must go through the certain specific things that we're going through for two reasons: (1) because the creator of this life wants us to see certain things, and each vision must be set up properly by a series of prerequisite visions and experiences, and (2) you can't go right to the 12th grade. You must go through grades K through 11 first. Although some skipping is possible, giant leaps aren't).

So now the question becomes: by the time you finish this book, will I have made the rewards so tantalizing and desirable that you'll have the strength to commit to making the changes necessary to achieving them? Will I have made the route so obvious that you'll have enough confidence and motivation to take it? Well, I think you'll each have to experience Hawaii for yourselves to feel the level of commitment that someone who's been there has. But I hope that I've inspired you to the point where your left lobe is saying "yeah that sounds good, and I think that there's something there for me". And then you'll try it and have the experience for yourself. Then you'll have the strength of these experiences to propel you on to greater heights and to give you the strength to say no to things that are bad for you (and for your affect on the rest of life). And all of these positive experiences will further sharpen and tune you into your sense of right and wrong, natural and unnatural, true and not true, real and unreal (which ultimately are all the same distinctions). And gathering these experiences will gather a positive momentum which will, in turn, create a snowball effect in the direction of normalcy, naturalness, cleanness and all of the positive experiences in life.

Now I can't transplant into you my LSD visions of God, love and realness. And if you didn't live in the 1950's, you won't be able to compare the feelings of the '60's, '70's, and '80's to it (although you can compare the fruit). And if you weren't in San Francisco in the late 1960's you won't really know what the hippie movement felt like and how it compares to all other efforts of 'people living together'. These are all my experiences. And although I've tried to give the positive sides of them to you, as best I can, to inspire you, now you need to use that inspiration to create your own positive experiences. Because these experiences will fuel your fire to want to create more and similar ones. And they will also give more validity to the rest of what I'm saying to you. Also you can tap into the positive experiences that you already have. Strength of commitment is a growing thing, whose growth can range from 'regression' to 'snowball'. Although, there is a common thread between us that makes my job a lot easier than trying to convince someone to go to Hawaii. And that is, we all have a truth meter, a deep down sense of what's true and what isn't.

All of the *positive* things that I just mentioned should serve well as motivators in helping us to do the work of transforming ourselves and our lives, and strengtheners during the work. But we can also be greatly motivated by *negative* feelings. For example, we should be inspired by the positive rewards of the great life that nature has carved out for us, but we should also feel guilt and shame for how we're hurting nature's creation by not living it. We should also feel fear for the immediate and after-life repercussions that nature might have in store for us for us going against it's great and powerful will. As a reaction to the guilt and shame we should feel a great remorse for the aberrant aspects of the life that we live, and then make a firm and solemn commitment to change our errant ways no matter what, for ourselves, our families, all of life, and the creator of life. These are the feelings that have the power to change lives.

Unfortunately, the way that many people live their lives is like in a boxing match. They go through the match using their own technique even though it may be faulty. Then when they finally get knocked down, they accept the hurt, suffer it, get back up and try to fight again *using the same technique.* But this technique that once got them hurt is going to again get them hurt until they eventually get knocked out. What I'm trying to encourage here is, before the next knockdown, **throw in the towel** (to nature). The opponent is **too** big and powerful. As a matter of fact, give up the boxing career altogether. Become a tag team wrestler, with nature as your partner and leader in the tag team. And then wrestle with all of the problems of your life.

One thing about being an author is that it doesn't have the immediate feedback like a conversation has. Immediate feedback in a conversation allows us to change the conversation around spontaneously so that we can effectively communicate to someone in a way that's tailor made to what they know and understand, what their experiences are, where they're at now, and where their interests are at. That's why I have to use an entire book and hope that I've covered all bases for everyone. But it's important to me to know how I'm affecting the reader, because there is something very important that I'm trying to accomplish here. I'm not just in the business of throwing out data and then trying to make money for my efforts. I want to see if my seeds are producing any flowers. So what I'm saying here is to please feel free to write to me through Lighthouse Publishing, if you are so inclined, and let me know if I've inspired or helped you in any way. Also let me know if there's something that you didn't understand, or some way that you feel that I could have been more effective.

Now as far as the Hawaii of this book goes, I'm going to spend the rest of this book continuing to charter the course for your boat to sail. Also, I'll need to show you how to make any needed repairs on the boat to get it in shape for the trip.

Chapter 18
The Right Environment

If your intention is to grow a flower,
you don't plant the seed in a desert.

Any form of life in it's infant stage is very fragile and delicate. A flower's very survival is dependent on the right balance of water, sunshine, shade, nutrients from the soil, and protection from other forms of life. And, actually, these needs continue on for the rest of it's life.

In the first part of the book I tried to give motivation to approach one's problems in another way by showing the errancy and camouflaged ineffectiveness of the drug approach, and also warning of it's many dangers. In the second part I tried to give direction and inspiration by defining what actions in life would produce a satisfied heart (which would have no use for drugs). Now I'm going to assume that you're all fired up and ready to make the changes.

As expressed in the flower analogy that I gave above, your first consideration is your environment. You must eliminate, as much as possible, the sources outside of yourself that tend to cause you to do unnatural things, tend to keep you from doing natural things, and tend to make it easy to take drug approaches. A growing flower doesn't want to have to deal with sandstorms, intense sun and Gila monsters. You need things to be calm and quiet, so that you can start seeing and dealing with the inclinations to do wrong that emanate from your invironment (by invironment I mean: the realm which is outside the experiencer {you} but is within your body, which includes: the subconscious mind, basic human nature, body inclinations, emotional impulses, etc., as I've described before).

So now as you carefully pick the setting for your growth, you have to determine what is healthy, and what is unhealthy. And when has something gone far enough and demands a change? And can it be fixed or not?

Let's start with a simple rule: Don't stay in an environment that makes you feel like you need drugs in order to stay in it. Now when I speak of not staying in the environment, I don't necessarily mean to physically leave. Sometimes all that needs to be changed is your perception of the environment, and how you should participate in it (which, in a sense, is changing the environment). I always want to stress exhaustive self-examination first, lest you unnecessarily hurt someone, or make a regrettable mistake that would hurt you. Make sure that you can't find fault in your contribution to the environment. People are bailing out of marriages too easily these days. I basically see a marriage as a lifelong commitment between two imperfect beings. Only in rare circumstances (like extramarital affairs) should there be divorce. If there are unbearable circumstances in a home, the extreme should be a separation, with the constant working towards reconciliation. But I also discourage this. Many times adversity is what is necessary to create change for the better in us. A vacuum might foster complacency, or worse yet, drugs and desperate unnaturalness to fill it's void.

The basic principle here is: in an unnatural situation you either have to (1) use a drug to silence your conscience (which will try to steer you back to a natural course), or (2) speak out against it, in an attempt to correct it's offness and restore it to a natural environment, and possibly cause conflict, or (3) leave the situation.

In the first option, you are either trying to perform, or continue to perform, some unnatural behavior, either to appease someone else's unnatural demands or your own misguided, unnatural demands. But for the normal-seeking person, this option isn't even considered, because they understand that this approach just keeps them from the real treasures in life and eventually causes serious problems. You either choose the second option, as a service to others involved (by giving them some honest feedback to think about) and to others in general (by making this world a cleaner place to live in), or you choose the third option if it's too dangerous or if there's no chance of anything productive that could come out of confronting the problems. But first make sure that it isn't something in **your** invironment that needs speaking out against. I'm only applying this rule to environments that are filled with unnaturalness, and that make 'unnatural behavior' a prerequisite for involvement in them. Also ones that aren't easily changeable. I don't consider marriage or parent/child relationships to be included as possibly being one of them because, although they can be very difficult at times, the bonds are too strong and we have a <u>responsibility</u> to help make these work well. Especially as a mate or a parent because we chose and helped to create these relationships. The following personal story is an example of the type of situation that I feel that we can and should leave.

Back when I was more under the control of my mind (as opposed to my heart), I let it talk me into taking a job away from my home for 3 weeks in a Reno casino. After much suffering and feeling like I had been sentenced for 3 weeks, my sister-in-law came into my work one night with her husband and they asked me to sit at the bar and have a drink with them. Sticking to my no-drug, stay-in-touch-with-reality policy I said "thanks, but I couldn't because I don't drink". Then they said "well at least sit at the bar and have an orange juice with us", and I said "o.k.". I sat there and sipped my orange juice as we talked. But slowly I started to notice that my weeklong feeling of suffering was gone and I was feeling happiness. I was pleasantly surprised. Then I started to notice that my cheeks were slightly numb and tingling. My confusion as to this transformation was cleared up when the bartender asked me "do you want another orange and amaretto?". Because my tolerance was so low from not having a drink (not even beer or wine) for many years before then, I was drunk. I was happy, everything was beautiful, and I loved everyone around me. And, for the first time at this job, I couldn't wait to get on stage and forget everything and just have fun. What heretofore had been an unpleasant experience was now not only bearable, but fun. When I finally got on stage, I attacked the music with a joy that I hadn't had all week before. My awareness gates were practically completely shut. But slowly I started getting a headache and the fountain of my joy was going down, and starting to sputter. I tried to force it back up, but it was no use. The ride was coming to an end and now it was time to pay the ticket. I suffered even worse than before through the remaining shows that night because now I was physically suffering, as well as emotionally. (Restating one of the themes of this book: it's not necessary to experience a downer in order to experience an upper. We just need to know which life actions will produce uppers without downers, {As I found out on this trip, working in a casino away from my family for 3 weeks isn't one of them} instead of trying to steal the uppers with drugs and then paying for our crime later). But in the heat of this situation, the thought occurred to me, if people use novacaine to block their awareness of pain during a dental appointment, then why couldn't I use alcohol as my medicine to get through this gig? Three things gave me my answer. (1) The hangover the next day, (2) the rush of guilt and conscience the next day, and (3) the drunk, vomiting 'local', whose car I had to drive home for them that night because they were unable to (this was evidence to me of what continuing in this pattern and building a tolerance would do). NEVERTHELESS I did occasionally have a drink for the rest of the gig because I didn't want the pain when it came on, and I knew that the gig would be over in 2 weeks. But during these 2 weeks I did notice myself starting to lose a lot of what I had accomplished inside over the years, and it took a little time to get back to normal. The moral of the story here is: <u>if you're not capable of staying in an environment without losing happiness or taking drugs, find the fault in it and remedy it, or leave it.</u> This could either mean (1) the fault is within you and you need to change your perceptions and attitudes, (2) the fault is outside of you and you need to attempt to change it, (3) the fault is outside of you and will not be changed, therefore you must leave the environment. But don't let it pull you under because it just keeps getting worse. That's the nature of drugs, as was described in chapter 7's discussion on tolerance.

As for the option of confronting people in the

aberrant environment around you with their offness, be sensitive to the level of their ability to objectively and constructively hear what you are saying (vs. having buttons pushed). I'm learning that it's wise to not confront people unless you know that they don't mind being confronted (although I will always put feelers out to test a person's level of confrontability because I think that confrontation is healthy and a good thing and is necessary to help us grow to higher levels). But you don't want to push their buttons and enter into the 'psychodrama zone' and engage their anger, defensiveness and argumentativeness. You would be in unrealness with a chance of a heavy confrontation that will only serve as a catharsis for them and a pain for you. I think that the best approach to this can be summarized in the Biblical story that I call "dust on the heels".

In the days when Jesus was alive it was hard times (only then you couldn't lock your door or move easily). There was fear of the Romans, immorality, and most of the religious leaders were corrupt. When Jesus came onto the scene, He was like an oasis for all that was good and right, and many followed Him. *Being* as in tune with nature as He was allowed people to experience and follow the goodness that was within them. He was a leader and a focal point as well as a teacher. But Jesus told His followers that there would be a time soon when they would be without Him. His followers were upset and asked how they would be able to cope with the evil that was rampant in the world. Here's how He told them to relate to others. He said not to compromise or hide the goodness that is within them, or that they know about. But also not to go into the evil cities. "And into whatever city or village you enter, inquire who is worthy in it, and abide there until you go away. And as you enter the house, give it your greeting. And if the house is worthy, let your greeting of peace come on it, but if it is not worthy, let your greeting of peace return to you. And whoever does not receive you or heed your words, as you go out of that house or that city, shake off the dust of your feet." and "whenever they persecute you in this city, flee to the next" (Matthew 10:11-14,23). Now what does this mean? It means that we should each be a center of goodness, and never compromise our goodness. Then find who else seems good and accept them and treat them as good. But if they should prove to be not so "let your greeting of peace return to you". And then walk away. Don't stay and endure their evil, or be in a situation where you have to hide what you see in order to keep peace. Also, don't be weak and succumb to them, because you'll just develop a tolerance for their evil and offnesses, and gradually probably find yourself doing the same things. Also don't argue or fight with them. And don't feel guilty about walking away. The parable simply says: walk away and brush them out of your heart the same way that you're going to brush the dust off of your heels (which was a sign of rejection in those days). What a liberating concept. We don't need to be tied to evil people. If you stay on a ship that is bent on sinking you will be sucked down also. This is not to say that you shouldn't make an attempt to bring a person or a situation to goodness, but don't waste your time in a situation that is not going to respond. Of course in a marriage, your attempt must be to the n-th degree being that this is a lifetime commitment, unless your mate has been unfaithful. This is not to say that a separation wouldn't sometimes be healthy, while simultaneously working on your marriage with a counselor, in order to take some of the heat off. But only in rare, extremely hostile, dangerous situations should this be necessary.

So now, what is a healthy environment? Let me put it another way: where do you think it would be best to plant a certain type of flower? Well, one safe place would be where other flowers of the same type are growing and flourishing. In other words, you should be around other people who are committed and determined to grow and be clean. Also, being in contact with people who have succeeded in achieving the higher states that we aspire to achieve is important for guidance and inspiration and a vision of what our next steps will be like. When I first started out as a musician, I wanted to be as good as I could be, yet I didn't like to practice and I would find it hard to motivate myself to do so. So what I would do is I would join bands in which everyone was older and better than I was. This forced me to come up to their level or be embarrassed or kicked out. When I would get to their level I'd then join a better band, etc., etc.. At any point in a growing situation, you want to be around motivated, determined, disciplined people who can inspire you and who you can also inspire.

In a sense, life can be a very lonely endeavor. That is, if you look at this planet from an over-viewpoint of 5 miles above it, you see very few people. What you do see is a lot of concrete, glass and wooden boxes, and moving metal and glass boxes. We know that there are people in all of these, but there is no direct contact when they are in these states. (And the problem here is that much unseen evil can go on behind closed doors). But being that we are social beings, we need to form relationships with other humans who dwell in these boxes. But because there are so many walls, we see few people. And because we see few people, our range of selection is very limited. Whereas, we should have a large selection of people to choose from to find the ones who best fit all of the nuances of our needs, and for whose needs we are best suited. Now I'm not saying that we can't create a large selection and find these optimum people for us, but it takes a lot of work and effort (which I highly encourage). But in most cases we're just like pinballs, haphazardly forming relationships with those who just happen to be around. What I'm saying here is that we have to be aggressive, patient and businesslike about finding the people for our relationships in life. But this all has to start with 'knowing what we're looking for'. So then how can we know the attributes of our perfect mate, the specifics of our perfect job, the location of the perfect city and neighborhood to live in, the perfect type of dwelling for us in it, the perfect friends, social groups, activities, etc. ? Well, if you want to know your heart's desires, let your heart show them to you in movie form, that is, through fantasizing. This can be done anywhere, but a good formal setting would be to go in your bedroom, close the door, turn off the light, lay on your bed, close your eyes and fantasize:

(1) Your job-and all of it's aspects. What are you doing, how do you feel about it, where does it take place, what are your hours, what is your boss (or are you the

boss), how much do you make, what are the potentials for growth, what are your ambitions and desires, etc..

(2) Your mate-(if you're single) what do they look like, what is their personality like, what are they into, what are their beliefs, how do they feel about children, what is their energy level, etc..

(3) Where you live-what city, house or apartment, urban or rural, dense or sparse, the climate, what's available there, etc..

(4) Your friends

etc., etc., etc..

And only pick fantasies that make you feel good, and that are in tune with nature's optimum design.
NOW MAKE THESE HAPPEN. Do whatever it takes.
After reading this book you'll have all of the answers that you'll need to successfully live this life. So therefore, if your life or anything about it isn't working, you have only yourself to blame. There is no room for complaining, only work.

Chapter 19
Getting Through Withdrawal

So now let's deal with the hardest part of making the transition from 'being attached to drugs and living a saccharin, problemated life' to 'living a happy, natural, satisfied life'. And that is, getting through withdrawal(s). This is the hump that, once gotten over and into a natural lifestyle, it would be just as hard to go back the other way. A person will need all of their determination, inspiration and commitment to get through it, as well as a lot of support from those around them (if they don't have supportive people around them, they should seek them out. There are many of them out there in anti-drug support groups, churches, etc.).

There are 2 types of addiction: mental and physical. And there are things that a person can do to help them withdraw from the momentum of both. The length and the intensity of the withdrawal will depend on the length of the addiction and the power of the drug(s). But **whatever it takes,** get through it. No matter how painful it is, you will make it. Many others have. Just accept the pain and see it as the penalty that you have to pay to nature for abusing it's ways (of course, there are things that you can do to make it bearable, which will be described in this chapter). And once it's over, it's over (that is if you've set up a natural environment and lifestyle). Besides, consider the alternatives: A lifelong drain of money, effort and health; inevitably having to go through it anyway; possibly death; the possible after-death consequences of suicide and/or a wasted life; the quality of life being missed out on, etc.. And there are more. Write down all of the pros and cons for going through withdrawal, and then talk yourself out of all of the cons. But I do want to restate here that you can't say no to drugs unless you have something more powerful and satisfying to say yes to. That's why I spent a great deal of a book about drugs spelling out the specifics of 'the natural lifestyle', which is the only lifestyle that our emotions will honor with peace and satisfaction, and not give us the emptiness, enturbulation and dissatisfaction that leads us to drugs.

So now if you've decided that you're going to go through withdrawal and get it over with, here are a few suggestions.

It might help, or even be necessary, to use a medically oriented facility that is designed to help you get through the physical part of withdrawal. It can give you an unencumbered environment, support, medicine, monitoring of your body functions to show progress and help in custom-designing your withdrawal program, an environment free from demands and pressures and people who might want to influence you in the other direction, a commitment that you are going to make it through and not be interrupted, staff to talk to, other people who are committed to ridding themselves of drugs who you can share mutual support with, etc.. The idea is that once you check in, you've made a commitment that you are going to finally rid yourself of drugs, and you won't have to deal with any counter-intention or wavering by yourself. Withdrawal is not an easy thing and once you get to the point that you've made your commitment, you want to do everything that you can to insure that you're going to make it. Protect your commitment and your plan to make a better life for yourself and those who are close to you. Also, medical insurance could possibly help out here.

Once you get the mental and physical resistance to a lower gradient of intensity (or if you're starting out there), here are some things that you can do.

When you absolutely feel like you can't stand the tension of fighting off what your body and mind wants you to go back to (cigarettes, drugs, alcohol, food, T.V., etc.), get up <u>immediately</u> and go out and do a <u>fun</u> form of exercise (basketball, tennis, bowling, golf, etc.). You'll relieve the tension, and focus your mind on something other than the pain while your body is healing. Plus it will speed up the physical process of elimination through sweating and higher rates of blood flow, respiration, etc..

But don't satisfy the tension by resorting to the drug. The feeling of wanting the drug feels very real and natural but it's not. If it were, we'd all feel like we had to have cocaine, a cigarette, heroin, etc.. It's just the inclination of an 'adjusted' body to stay in the groove that it's created (through enzymes, cell change, internal chemical changes, etc.) to lessen the intensity of the shock and unpleasant reactions to drugs (in the case of physical addictions), and to avoid facing suppressed feelings and emotions (in the case of mental addictions). If you make it through the withdrawal period, and you've learned how to create the natural, satisfying lifestyle that won't create a desire for drugs within, you're free. But 'feelings' are a strange and delicate phenomena. Only the person experiencing them knows the intensity of the resistance that they are dealing with. This is why another person can't just tell someone to do something and expect that they can do it. This is why each person who wants to rid themselves of drugs must custom‑design their own withdrawal plan, and continue to adjust it in midstream. But I feel like, in this book, I've given all of the tools necessary for anyone to form a successful plan to rid themselves of drugs.

Here are some other actions that a person can do to help them deal with the short-range tensions of withdrawal: exercise, games, massage, sleep, conversations, nature outings, formal meditation, spot meditation, community service, church, involvement in community groups, music (playing or listening), classes, tapes (audio and/or video), television (try to limit this to only programs where there's a natural feeling), going out, or whatever else that you can imagine. But get through it once and for all and don't ever flirt with the inclination to go back.

But, once again, the new natural life (environment, relationships, jobs, ways of relating to your insides, ways of relating to others, etc.) that you're building is what will ultimately free you from drugs permanently. I mean you're not going to opt for dog food if you've got a refrigerator filled with prime rib.

Chapter 20
Knowing Your 'Natural' Self

Who (and what) are we really? What is this life all about? What approach can we take towards life so that we can maximize the ups and minimize the downs, while all through this maintaining a peace and satisfaction, whereby we won't ever feel an inclination towards drugs? Is this even possible? Yes it is, And my aim here is to show how this can be accomplished.

First, the first question: Who (and what) are we really? Let's take a most objective, most basic look at being in this existence. We each individually *find* ourselves inside a human body which has a specific design and a specific set of rules governing it. We are able to take this human body around on a planet populated with other humans and interact with them in natural physical settings and within systems and structures that other humans have created (and are creating). The planet is a part of a giant universe that we humans have no authority over and had no authorship in, and have no direct knowledge of who does or did. Also, we have no direct knowledge of who designed our bodies, this planet, or the specific details of both.

Now for the next question: What is this life all about? Now that we know that we are indelibly trapped inside these bodies within this existence, and that it's of no use to try to struggle to get out, the next thing is to accept it, try to understand it, and work out an optimum game plan for existing in it. We need to know as much as we need to know about this existence so that we can devise a game plan that will maximize the pleasure and sense of positive purpose that we can experience in it, and minimize the waste and the pain. So then, how do we go about attaining this knowledge?

First you must be able to discern which knowledge is important to this endeavor, and which is superfluous. The important knowledge is called wisdom. The author of this creation wouldn't have been very fair or loving had He* not made available to us all of the knowledge that we would need in order to live our lives correctly. (* For those who have a problem with 'He' being used: 'He' is used by those who see God's relationship to us as being analogous to the functions of a loving, earthly father who loves us, looks out for us, is concerned about our growth, and imparts wisdom to us.) Therefore, the knowledge (wisdom) that is important, is that which will allow us to live our lives abundantly, positively, with a minimum of turmoil, and allow us to fulfill whatever the purpose of our life is in the giant scheme of this creation.

So then specifically, what knowledge is important to us? The knowledge of the rules for optimum workability of the human vehicle that we live in (which includes mind, body, emotions and spirit) and the specific ways that it's behavior manifests when it is optimumly inter-relating with the physical and spiritual universe around it that it is interdependent with. If we knew these rules, we would know which actions are going to lead to harm (of self and others), and which actions would lead to the inner satisfaction of knowing that what we're doing is right (and most of the time: peace, joy, happiness and fulfillment. But not always because we can't control the actions of those around us). We would be able to properly flow with our natural inclinations, and fulfill our natural drives, as they occur, in the precise manner that they were designed to optimumly and peacefully function within ourselves and within life. We need to introduce a rules-censor into our behavior because (1) over the course of our lives, we've custom-designed something that didn't need to be custom-designed (our natural inclina-tions), and (2) within the basic nature of a human being is selfishness (which is the antithesis of love) that needs to be brought under control so that we can all peacefully live together with no one being taken advantage of. We need to very specifically know the rules that concern our function and purpose in the greater schemes of this life (family, business, social and universal).

Let's take a look at the primary medium where the work of learning, understanding, bridling, self-control, seeking, programming, re-programming, evaluating, analyzing, etc. takes place: our brain. One of the functions of the brain is to operate our bodies without conscious awareness. If we had to consciously perform all of the functions that we do...well, it would be impossible. Our brain is like a master computer, whereby the operater presses one button and a whole series of responses occur. We initiate a thought command and/or outside stimuli is presented to us, and a whole series of subconscious brain responses are set off that we had no conscious role in (but the conscious now has an opportunity to respond in this mental chess game, as described at the beginning of chapter 5). This is a natural, necessary process that only becomes a problem when what is being kicked out of the subconscious is 'demands for unnatural behavior'. The unfortunate thing here is that many of these subconscious response-programs were programmed in under duress and against our natural inclinations (to appease the unnatural demands of the 'giants' {parents and older children are giants to children}, or those who have some power over us such as bosses, mates, etc., out of fear of physical and/or emotional harm). So maybe we kept peace with the outside, but now we have inner turmoil. That is, now there is a battle for our actions between our subconscious-automatic-response-computer and our natural inclinations. This battle, and the wish to quiet it, is the number one reason why people take drugs. The wise observation here though is: one of these is changeable and the other one isn't. Learning to reprogram the unnatural inclinations of the subconscious, and to live out the natural inclinations as intended is the only real solution to this inner battle and the emotional turmoil that it causes.

So now, how do we go about reprogramming our unnatural inclinations? The reprogramming *process* was described at the beginning of chapter 5. Now I want to address how we discover what to program in. First of all, the mind is a very *active* and *thirsty* critter. So we need to quench it's thirst by *focusing* it on something. If reprogramming to naturalness is our intention, then we need to *focus* on books, tapes, videos, films, speakers, etc. that can educate us as to what naturalness is. I'll talk more about this in the next chapter. If we don't take charge and focus our mind, it will find it's own thing to focus on or it just might regurgitate some of the unnatural garbage that's already in our brain. The mind is like an infant that constantly seeks stimulation and something to play with, and whom we must steer away from the dangerous objects in the house. We must treat our minds the same way that we look out for our babies.

As far as the *active* nature of our mind goes, focusing will handle that. But there is another way of dealing with it, and another way of learning. We've pretty much been talking about *left lobe* learning here. But they say that a picture is worth a thousand words. The *right lobe* operates in non-verbal impressions such as pictures, feelings, etc. and can show us a lot. I mean, what good is having verbal knowledge if you can't *see* the meaning of it? So now how can we go about *seeing* the truths of this life? First we must quiet down the active, thirsty left lobe (by the way, the left lobe loves these *visions* of truth and has a positive, constructive field day with the flood of new high level data that they produce). We need to quiet it down so that we can just look, without thought or criticism, at what really is. (I mean, it's kind of hard to see a movie if you're running up and down the aisles and constantly running out of the theatre). We can accomplish this stilling of the mind through meditation. That is, focusing our mind on something, with our eyes closed, to keep it still, so that our experiential side can *see* what's actually going on, without our mind defining it (based on it's programs), causing an emotional response, trying to propel us to action, etc.. We need to go into this endeavor completely with an *open mind*, in the strictest sense of the term. We want to start with the assumption that our lives aren't completely working and therefore there's something wrong with the ways that we are seeing and responding to things. Therefore, until we know where the problems really are, we don't want to trust anything that our mind is saying at this point. It makes sense to us that the natural way would be the correct way to live, and now we just want to look at nature directly, without any preconceptions or ongoing judgments, to get to know it better.

Focusing on our breath, and all of it's most minute details, is the best form of meditation. And the way that you do it is to just observe it. Don't (1) manipulate it, or (2) think about it. The whole point is that while you've got your mind tied down focusing on your breath and not leading you around by the nose and filling your consciousness with activities and thoughts, your right lobe will be able to *see* what's *really* going on in this life. And these visions will be so clear and real and feel so good that they'll give you a lot of power to be able to reprogram out a lot of the untrue things in your mind. Only the truth will set you free. If you choose to use meditation as a tool in your growth, you should introduce it to yourself with the following approach so that you're sure to get the benefits of it and not misjudge it. It should be done formally as a discipline for one hour every morning and evening. Just remember, there may be some uncomfortable squirming and fidgitiness when first trying to calm the mind down, but this will be far outweighed by the feelings of love, joy and awe at the visions that you'll see when your mind is still, and the liberating work that they will do.

Spot meditation can also be done throughout the day at various points if you feel that the mind is getting too active. Merely, in the middle of any activity, if you feel the mind getting too wound up or trying to propel you into an unnatural feeling action, stop the train of thought and focus on your breath. I mean, we have to 'pay attention' (look at) something. If we recognize or get a sense that our line of thoughts are going to bring trouble or negativity to us, we need to pay total attention to our breath. This will stop the line of thought's momentum and, eventually, the line of thought altogether. This is like your 'brakes' in growth. Of course, they will only stop you. The problem that you are having there still has to be dealt with on a verbal level and reprogramming must be done. Living life like this continually would only prove to be very boring, suppressive and frustrating. Remember, you don't want to turn meditation into a drug. It's just a *temporary* buffer to slow down the gradient of the barrage of problems and uncleannesses that will come; or it's just a tool to stop what you can instantly recognize as being 'off' trying to come on; or it's just a visionary aid. But it's not to become a crutch or a drug. Only use it as a stepping stone if you are **inspired** to, not because you **think** it would be good. But it's good to have these brakes and formal meditation as tools available to us because the mind has a huge momentum after many years of aberrated living and wrong programming and it will take some time and work to bring it under submission. A poet once said that many battles are won and lost on many different battlegrounds, but some of the greatest ones no one will ever see. And these are the ones that go on within us.

After practicing meditation for a while, hopefully what you will *see* is that you are not in conscious control over your breath process and heartbeat (at least to the point where you could totally stop them and live), your blood circulation, digestive system, etc.. You're not as much of an authority over yourself as you think. So then who or what is? Obviously the one that designed and created you and all of this existence. The valuable part of this kind of meditation is that this is not just going to be an intellectual realization now that you can swap for the next philosophical or religious fad that comes along. No, you'll be *looking* at reality. And once you've seen the truth, you've seen it. And seeing and knowing that you are not controlling your body is a valuable experience that you can build off of for the rest of your life. It also experientially puts you in touch with the willful decisions of the one who has the power over your bodily processes and feelings. These places that you meditate on are direct places where you can actually look for clues as to who's in control here. And the more that you look, the more that you see this power's modes of operation and purposes. And what you are looking at is reality that a left lobe (yours or other's) debate can't take away. And once you know where and how to look, as you continue to look there, you will begin and continue to see many more valuable things about that power and your relationship to it, as well as develop a healthy fear and awe about it. To those who already accept (heart and mind) the existence of God, instead of meditation, I recommend prayer (and I don't mean the repetitive, rote prayers that some religions have. I mean directly talking to God, asking Him for forgiveness, help, guidance, thanking Him, etc.. Refer to the Bible for guidelines on prayer).

It's kind of like living life in a concrete reservoir with a long high fence surrounding it, feeling very bored and dissatisfied with the lack of beauty and real activity in your environment. Then one day, you're walking along and you see a little peephole in one of the fences. You go over and look through the peephole and are amazed because you see a very beautiful world filled with lush gardens and flowers. And when you get over your initial excitement, you just want to stay and look at the beauty because of the wonderful feeling that it gives you. Then after basking in this feeling of beauty for a while, you realize that somebody over there created all of this, and is in charge over there. You feel their presence through the design of what they've created. Then all of a sudden, you feel this power speaking to you through the peephole from where they reside in the garden. What it's showing you feels like the highest wisdom that you've ever encountered, and the feeling that accompanies it is the most beautiful feeling that you've ever felt. And this power is ready and willing to show you many more important things about your life and how to create beauty within it. It speaks in feeling impressions, which in turn trigger words in your mind that verbally explain what you have seen, and what it means.

Now this is a constant relationship that can be tapped into any second, 24 hours a day, for the rest of our lives. It's amazing and very wonderful when you realize and *see* that the power that created us and this universe has made itself continually available to us and is not cut off from us. The question then becomes: do we make ourselves available to it, or do we cut ourselves off? Meditation will calm the impulsive, jumpy side of your self down and hold you at the peephole long enough for you to see the beauty, fall in love with it, better understand it's creator, and develop your ability to turn to and listen to the power that runs you.

But now you don't want to get into the meditation trap and turn it into a drug. Because as well as knowing the higher feelings and visions of this life {right lobe}, we

174

need to verbally understand them {left lobe} so that we can (1) reprogram our subconscious, (2) communicate it to others and (3) quickly tap visions { through outside verbal means such as books, tapes and other people } that would otherwise take a long time to come by through meditation. I'm a very analytical, inquisitive, leave-no-stone-unturned, satisfy-every-question-and-feeling type person and I have proven to myself that everything that happens to us in this life is cosmically ordained and authored, and all for a *good* purpose. Therefore we need to keep both the heart *and mental* channels open for communications to come through, and for transforming work to be done. A meditative focus can turn into a drug that we might end up sweeping important messages from the cosmos under.

Another thing that you will hopefully come to see in your meditation (or otherwise) is that those precious commodities: our feelings, are predesigned reactions also. So, knowing this, we can discover much about our Creator's will **first hand**, without reading any books or listening to any person, by seeing how He designed our feelings to react in certain situations. This can be a very scientific endeavor without any belief or faith involved. And it is very detailed and all-pervasive in our lives. Whether we want to acknowledge it or not, we have a continuous dialogue and relationship inside of ourselves with the designer of the specifics of what our feeling-responses are going to be. It is very wise and liberating when we realize that all of His intentions are good, and that we should **always** give Him priority and yield to Him.

So now the all important question is: If the designer of this life holds the power of us experiencing peace, love, satisfaction, happiness and pleasure, <u>what are the specific actions that are required for those precious feelings to be released?</u>

175

Chapter 21
The Handbook Of
The Rules Of Your Heart

Now the truth meter isn't an answer emanater. It's two-positioned feedback consists of 'thumbs up' and 'thumbs down'. Although we do have an answers-to-life-emanater within us, it is very incomplete. And it also has a hard time battling through our concepts and habitual, aberrant, impulsive mental reactions (and the resultant emotions that they create). It is much easier and expedient to our growth to just read or hear the truth, and then let our truth meter verify it or deem it to be untrue. Also our sense of logic may want to be satisfied here. But the truth meter is a simple yes-or-no gut reaction, and once we've proven it's credibility and developed a trust and respect for it, we grow that much quicker.

I used to be involved in a spiritual group that evolved out of India that practiced meditation, which in essence is an attempt to shut the aberrant inclinations of the mind, emotions and will off and just allow the natural inclinations to come through. But some of the fruit of this community was: a lot of unsuccessful male-female relationships, lack of business success, etc.. In other words, what I'm trying to say here is: being in touch with the truth meter in and of itself is not enough. It doesn't emanate answers (as to what the natural order is) quick enough to keep us from stumbling and possibly falling hard and hurting ourselves and others, in the meantime while we're learning. We need a way to know what nature's optimum design and all of it's intricate specifics are now, so that we can then have them either verified or deemed untrue by the truth meter, and then mold our lives to these optimum working principles. We need to know the specific actions that we need to make now so that our lives don't become filled with suffering from negative emotional feedback trying to warn us of the errancy of our actions, and so that our basic relationships can survive, thrive and not fall apart in the meantime while we try to grow. A mechanic's intentions may be good, but if he doesn't have a manual or an understanding of the problems (and the solutions) of your car, the results can be disastrous and even life threatening (as I've experienced with certain mechanics). Or can you imagine being handed a saxophone and being told to make music without being given an instructional manual? Worse yet, and being put on stage in front of a *paying* audience immediately? Well that's the situation that we're in. We have many people in our lives that are *paying* with their time, money, feelings, work, and need(s) invested in us. Are we making beautiful music, are we making bad music, or are we just standing there trying to figure out how to even make music at all?

So now, is there a place or a person or a magical book or cassette where we can get the specifics of nature's optimum design? Being very much a fan of all of the aforementioned feelings and very much a disliker of pain and negative feelings, I continued my search to find these answers and, of course, hoping that there was one magical place where I could find them all at once. A place where I could just totally submit, be transformed, and live happily ever after. I tried practically everything that the world had to offer, always hoping that my truth meter would give me a giant thumbs up in one of them. I delved into: positive thinking, psychology (many traditional and modern forms), philosophy, psychiatry, scientology, humanism, hedonism, holistic psychotherapy, counter-culture groups, group therapy, drug therapy, primal therapy, money, the music scene, psychics, eastern religion, etc.. In searching and trying out different forms, a good sense of logic and a very analytical, leave-no-stone-unturned approach (which I practiced all through my searching) will keep a person from getting stuck in a trip that doesn't have all the answers, and keep them moving on until they find the one that does. For instance, an alarm should go off when two pieces of data contradict each other and can't exist in the same space at the same time. Logically, only one of them can be true. But the problem that many people get into in their search for the truth, is that they so badly want the answers and for the search to be over that they accept an approach, suppress the feedback from their truth meter and sense of logic, put the blinders on (which is really shutting nature out), and then _act_ as if they've found it. But their actions and vibe will usually tell you that they haven't ("you shall know a tree by it's fruit"). They really aren't solidly experiencing peace in a relaxed way. Like Yogi Berra said "It ain't over 'til it's over". Not until you've arrived at the real truths of the specifics of the design of this creation and yourself will you experience that certain peace inside. I mean, you may get your carburetor rebuilt at a great carburetor shop, but your car still won't run great until _all_ of it's systems are running great. That is, each growth group has some good things to offer, but a whole working picture is needed for our lives to work great. You can even have a _perfect_ carburetor and your car still may not be able to run at all. It has been said that we have a God-sized void in us that only a knowledge of and a relationship with God can fill. No matter how much food, drugs, entertainment, T.V., ego, action, hyperness, etc. that we try to cram into it, only a true relationship with the author and designer of ourself and the universe can fill it and bring satisfaction (I mean who better would know the specifics of the design than the designer?).

So now, once again: is there a place where all the specifics of the design are written out, or do we just have to discover them by trial and error while listening to our truth meter? With great joy I'm able to tell you that yes, there is such a book, that describes the specifics of ourselves and this life in great detail. And that book is: "The Bible".

My analytical mind, heart and truth meter have verified this to me over and over and over again. Not to mention the peace, love, joy and satisfaction that I've been being filled with, as I focus on it, learn, understand and put into practice it's principles (now who else but God would have the power to create those feelings in me? Certainly not I, because I tried that approach).

Unfortunately, the Bible has gotten so much bad p.r.

(public relations) that people have become very skeptical and cynical about it (surprisingly, many people don't know the difference between the Bakkers and Jerry Falwell, or charismatics and fundamentalists). The reason that I came to the Bible last was because of the cold, ritualistic, empty, dogmatic Catholic upbringing that I had. This is the kind of religion that Karl Marx had in mind when he said that "religion is the opiate (drug) of the people". But these things aren't true Christianity. Let Jesus speak for himself (in the Bible). Realize that if you are cynical or skeptical about Christianity it's because of the people and organizations that have claimed to represent it. But they fall short of the Biblical standard. Jesus even said "see to it that you are not misled, for many will come in my name". He also said "beware of the false prophets who come to you in sheep's clothing but inwardly are ravenous wolves". Your relationship with God is one on one, directly between Him and you. And your relationship with His Bible is also one on one. No one can get inside of your truth meter, your heart or your sense of logic but you and Him, unless you let them. Check the Bible out and see for yourself. And find a good Bible teaching church (they're hard to find). You'll be in holy company (remember chapter 18-'The Right Environment'), and the teaching and the people there can help you to understand the Biblical principles (but remember, above all, don't abandon your truth meter or sense of logic, because all people have some imperfections. Only God doesn't).

In reading the Bible, start by reading what Jesus had to say. Get a red letter edition (where everything said by Jesus is in red letters). You will hopefully come to see that what He said, and where He was coming from was too wise and too perfect to have been said by a mere mortal. Besides, if He lied when He said that He and He alone was God incarnate, then that makes everything else that He said suspect. But your truth meter will show you that nothing else that He said (that our mortal minds can logically deal with) is suspect (which gives credibility to everything else that He said). Also, the history of his birth, life, ministry, miracles, death, burial and resurrection are not only verified by His disciples and followers, but also by the Roman and Jewish historians of the day. And giving your life to Him is a liberation, not an imprisonment. A liberation from having to figure this life out, or from making many bad moves. A liberation from having to depend on those who intend evil. Once you've verified His perfectness to yourself, you (in trust) just start obeying His teachings. This, in turn, will give you more confidence in Him when you see the magic that this obedience performs in your life and your feelings. And nothing else in this life can do this for you. He is the highest focus and the total truth. Everything else is just a percent of 'total truth' and the highness that He is. But definitely read what He says in the Bible. My testimony and words are not going to wholly liberate you. You have to start seeing Him for yourself, and letting the beauty of what He says, where He's coming from, and who He is show itself to you. And the only way that this can start to happen is if you expose yourself to His teachings. Read the "Sermon on the Mount" (Matthew 5-7). My favorite way to start getting into the Bible was to get a Ryrie Study Bible and look in the back in the topical index and scan to see whatever topic was close to my heart and my life at the time, and which specifics of nature's optimum design that I needed to know for the certain areas that I was having problems in. This can also be done with Nave's Topical Bible, where the Biblical verses are printed under the topical headings which are listed in alphabetical order. See if what the Bible has to say hits you as the wisest things that you've ever heard. It did me (and still does). Not only has it totally blessed my life and my experience, but I've yet to find anything that I can scientifically (logically) prove wrong or contradictory. This is what makes me believe that the rest of it is also true. Dig into it and see if the designer of your heart will magically open your eyes and reveal it's meanings to you, and show you that the author of The Bible and your heart are one and the same (be patient if you don't understand it at first). I've been doing it for 6 years now and I just keep getting cleaner, higher, happier, more at peace, more satisfied, less prone to doing stupid things, more able to do the best actions that I can do in my life, more able to live with and accept myself and others (and know which parts are acceptable and which aren't), etc.. But at rock bottom, this whole time I've had a basic peace and satisfaction that I'm involved with the highest thing that I could possibly be involved with anywhere in this life. It's like, as soon as I found the Bible and it hit me, I knew that my searching days were over. The unsettled, unsatisfied yearning that I had carried for many years was finally gone. There are <u>no more</u> questions. Only a constant stream of beautiful answers and understandings (and many more waiting in the wings). And, as is important to this book, not only have I had the power to say no to drugs, but I haven't even had any inclination to say yes. As a matter of fact, drugs are repulsive to me and would only bring me down.

Chapter 22
Higher And Higher Naturally

This is the clearest, most concise way that I can describe growth. It is said that of our mental functioning, our conscious mind is 10% of it and our subconscious mind is 90%. This has to be somewhat of an accurate approximation because there are so many physical, mental and emotional actions going on in us simultaneously that, in our limited conscious capacity, we couldn't possibly concentrate on each one of them and do them all at once. So we must rely on the computer-automatic-pilot-functionability of our brain. The automatic responses to stimuli that are stored in our computer's memory banks have been programmed in all of our life. But like any new computer, there are many functions that it must perform, and therefore the bulk of it's programming is required to be done in it's early stages (when particular responses are required in specific areas). After the initial responses are programmed in then it becomes a matter of 'editing' to change them, and any computer programmer or operator will tell you that editing is much harder than programming (but I have showed how to do that in this book). Nature has seen to it that all of the programming needed by a person will naturally and properly occur at it's proper time. But nature's timing of when this programming should be done and it's predetermined contents (which are in tune with nature's optimum design) can be undermined by hostile, tragic, unnatural, unwise, demanding, pressure environments. So what happens if we're somehow lucky enough to change to a higher environment, or we come upon a large volume of wisdom (such as the Bible) and we want to transform to these higher planes? (This happens with drugs too. Drugs, especially the heightened-awareness drugs, may give us visions and experiences of higher, more relaxed planes to live on, and then, after experiencing them we don't want to go back and live on the lower planes. But this is also one of the *problems* with drugs. We're supposed to <u>gradually</u> have our eyes opened so that the inspiration from these realizations will lead us to subconscious and behavior changes that we can realistically make without too much trouble). So now the dilemma is this. We're sitting on a higher plane recognizing the grossness and the ugliness of some of what our automatic pilot pushes out (speaking of gradual realizations, how many even realize that these gross and ugly impulses within us {with the exception of the ones that are due to selfishness} are <u>inanimate</u> recordings that were pressured on us, and are not really us, and that we should not take them personally? {But we do need to take responsibility for having them and for the aberrant actions that they produce}). What can we do to transform them?

I equate this with having an unclean pond filled with worms that are creating havoc within and without, and we are sitting on the banks of this pond. (The 'we' in this analogy is the conscious mind, the pond is the subconscious, and the worms are the aberrant programs that are within it). What we can do is just sit there and pluck out the worms as they show themselves, and get rid of them. (Many times you won't have to reprogram something in though because 'what comes naturally', in the given area, will do that by default and will be the optimum replacement. And, vice versa, when you program something good in it, automatically will push some worms out that are trying to occupy the same space that it's going to occupy). This whole process is just recognizing the lower-consciousness attitudes, perceptions, inclinations, concepts, impulses, emotional responses, philosophies, beliefs, values and interpretations that we have, and replacing them with greater wisdom that we've come into contact with. Simultaneously, we should be seeking higher and higher wisdom, because this will automatically motivate and energize 'worming' expeditions.

Keeping in mind that our responses and feelings are based on the 100% rather than just the 10% conscious mind (plus what's on the surface of the subconscious), you might ask: "is there a quicker way to clean out the pond than plucking each worm out individually ?" The answer is, yes. Brain physiology tells us that all of the data in our subconscious mind is intricately networked together. Therefore certain beliefs are foundational and common to a number of attitudes and spontaneous responses. If you change one belief, you simultaneously alter many other related attitudes and responses. It's like, if you kill the queen worm, many more will die. Also there are higher and more concise, condensed forms of wisdom that, in a few sentences, contain many paragraphs of wisdom. After all of my searches for experiential and intellectual wisdom (which has been many and extensive, and spans a little over 20 years and most of what the world has to offer) I wish to make this statement to you: the Bible has the highest and most concise, condensed wisdom on this planet. The speediest way to grow that I know is to just read it a lot (the New Testament and Proverbs are good places to start). Also go to a church that just teaches the Bible literally and has a good, knowledgeable teacher who can illuminate and clarify what the Bible is saying. I feel very fortunate to have found the church that I go to (Grace Community Church in Sun Valley, California) and the pastor who teaches there (John MacArthur). I generally come out of each service filled with love and joy and a relaxed peace. What happens while I'm in there makes the moment when I come out the highest point of my week. You see, by subjecting yourself to this highly condensed wisdom, you allow a spiritual worm exterminator to go into your pond and do a lot of work for you that you don't even see being done. Logic tells us that there can be only one truth, and knowing more and more of this truth will gradually make us freer and freer (that is, free from the bondage and destructive works of ignorance). Focusing on God's Word is the best thing that we can do. And this isn't natural to the aberrant grooves of our automatic pilot, so it requires some discipline to 'prime the pump' and get us to go to church, or put on a tape (Grace Church puts out some great ones) in the car or at home, or watch a video tape (secular television won't give you this kind of peace), or go to a Bible study. I try to constantly be focused on the Word in the above mentioned activities and in my thinking. Not just because of a particular discipline, or because I'm trying to accomplish something, but also because it makes me *feel* better than anything else I can do. This world and my mind had their shot and they failed miserably and brought me many problems. I try not to give them my time anymore. Now most of what this world has to offer, through it's media, feels bad to me, because it's so heavily polluted with ignorance, unnaturalness and evil. The negative feelings that I used to have as a response to the sinful things in the world I used to sweep under the drug so that I could exist in it with a pseudo-peace. But I'm living in a different Kingdom now, and I allow myself to recognize these negative feelings (they were always there anyway), and now I understand why I'm having them and why a lot of what the world has to offer is distasteful. The Bible says that God is love, but it also says that God **hates** sin (sin is another name for what I've been calling 'unnaturalness'). It's natural and optimum that we have these feelings.

Also, get involved in church groups and live out the advice being given in the Bible. It will fill your heart to do so, and also make you strong and happy. Needless to say, drugs will be the furthest thing from your mind and only an intrusion. Prayer, service, fellowship and studying the Word will become your new highs.

The funny thing about 'experiences' is that you can't just see them in a store window or in a catalogue and pick them out. You have to try the actions that bring them on to know what they are. The tragedy about today's media is that the actions that will bring bad experiences and destroy lives are getting the most air time. While the normal, natural ones that will bring good experiences and fix lives are getting the least.

So I hope that I've been of help to you in this book. And I very deeply and sincerely hope that I've persuaded you to try the approach that I've laid out in it. I hope that I've opened your eyes, given you a direction, inspired you, and showed you the streams as well as the bears. As for me, well you know where you can find me, sitting by the pond hunting for worms, and then reaping the rewards by being able to swim in a pond that's getting cleaner and clearer (and enjoying doing the pondmaker's work).

Index

Bibliography

Bible. English. *New American Standard*. 1978.

Capra, Frank. *The Name Above the Title* (an autobiography). Random. 1985.

Cavasina, Richard. *A Self Instructional Module Regarding the Effects of Abused Drugs*. California: R & E Research Associates. 1982.

"Creativity and the Troubled Mind", *Psychology Today*, Volume 21 number 4, April 1987.

Horney, Karen. *Our Inner Conflicts*. New York: Norton. 1966.

"Just Say No Foundation Eases Children's Fears". *Los Angeles Daily News*. June 30,1987.

"New Team Gears Up For War On Drugs". *Los Angeles Daily News*. July 20,1986.

Webster's New World Dictionary, Second College Edition. New York: The World Publishing Company. 1970.

Notes

R FORM

E PUBLISHING
)-B
RESEDA, CA 91335-220 U.S.A.
Telephone: (818) 345-7586

"SWEEPING IT UNDER THE DRUG" $9.95

Californians: Please add 60¢ sales tax per book or submit a Resale
Card to us.

Shipping $1.00 for the first book and 50¢ for each additional book

_____ I can't wait 3-4 weeks for Book Rate Mail. Here is $3.00 per book
for Air Mail

DISCOUNT SCHEDULE

1 Book — No Discount
2-4 Books — 20% Off
5-9 Books — 30% Off
10-24 Books — 40% Off
25-49 Books — 42% Off

50-74 Books — 44% Off
75-99 Books — 46% Off
100-199 Books — 48% Off
200 or More Books — 50% Off

_____ Books Ordered at $9.95 each .... _____

Sales Tax _____

Shipping _____

TOTAL (enclosed) _____

Name: _____

Address: _____

City & State: _____ Zip: _____